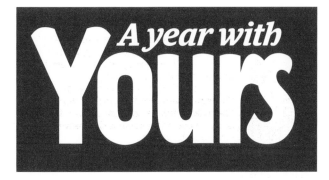

Name
Address
Postcode
Home phone
Mobile phone
Email

In case of emergency, contact:

Name
Telephone

USEFUL CONTACTS

BANK	
BUILDING SOCIETY	
CHEMIST/PHARMACY	
CHIROPODIST	
COUNCIL	
CREDIT CARD EMERGENCY	
DENTIST	
DOCTOR	
ELECTRICIAN	
GARAGE	
HAIRDRESSER	
HOSPITAL	
LOCAL POLICE	
MILKMAN	
OPTICIAN	
PLUMBER	
SOLICITOR	
TAXI	
VET	

RENEWAL REMINDERS

	RENEWAL DATE	POLICY NUMBER	TELEPHONE
CAR INSURANCE			
CAR TAX			
MOT			
HOME INSURANCE			
TV LICENCE			
PET INSURANCE			
Yours SUBSCRIPTION			

THE YEAR AHEAD

What's in the

Astrologer Lynne Ewart shares her predictions for the year ahead

ARIES

MARCH 21 - APRIL 20

As the first sign of the zodiac, and a fire sign, too, you often get plunged into new situations where you have to have all your wits about you, finding the way, not just for yourself, but often for others too! You are never knowingly found lacking in courage, drive or initiative, and your adventurous spirit can exhaust lesser mortals!

You may be impatient at times, and you might not always stop and think too much about what others are doing, because you don't like to pry, but the minute you are asked for help, you are without a doubt the zodiac's kindest giver, not thinking of yourself, only of the challenge in front of you.

THIS YEAR could begin with an air of nostalgia, or a sentimental quest, but then Venus, planet of love, beauty and money, spends four months, instead of the usual few weeks, visiting your sign between February and June, and this could see you reconnecting with people you've not seen in years, and thoroughly enjoying yourself. A few fences may be mended, too. There may be exciting sparks and plans for adventures being rekindled for some! Jupiter is opening doors and you'll feel that your world is widening. Creative Ariens will excel.

A THOUGHT FOR THE YEAR: Never say never in this rollercoaster year of surprises!

TAURUS

APRIL 21 - MAY 21

You like your life to feel smooth and orderly, to know where you're pointed, preferably well in advance, because you don't take comfortably to being herded along too swiftly! If you decide to up the pace, you can be astounding as you bound along, but it has to be of your own choosing. You tend to mull things over for a time, before you commit, because you don't like to veer off course once you have committed to a plan.

Stubborn is a word often attributed to your sign's nature, but that same energy can equally mean you're reliable, steadfast and focussed. People know what to expect from you, and like an oak tree, Taurus is often found giving much-appreciated shelter and being the rock for others to lean on.

THIS YEAR could bring some restructuring, perhaps due to what's happening with another, and there'll be many a Taurus who's going to become more of a 'power behind the throne', supporting or balancing the books for a relative. Equally you might make this the year when you decide to shock a few folk by signing up for a course that'll enrich your life and, perhaps, your understanding of others, too. Health linked interests could appeal.

A THOUGHT FOR THE YEAR: A loved one delights you by fulfilling a dear ambition.

stars for 2017?

GEMINI

MAY 22 – JUNE 21

The classic Gemini has a marvellous sense of youthful interest in what's coming next, usually not so keen on looking back, unless it's to have a giggle at old photos. Gemini likes to think positively about life, no matter how tough it might get, and you don't easily share your deeper feelings, mostly because you prefer not to dwell there. You can go long periods of time without being in touch with friends and then quite easily, just pick up where you left off. Restless and forever on the move, you don't always pay full attention, simply extracting what's of interest and scooting on in your conversations, which usually head off in multiple directions. Gemini is vivacious, lively and never dull!

THIS YEAR may at times feel challenging yet rewarding, particularly if you are hoping to do something quite different as part of a team or a couple. Indeed relationships are under the rays of 'let's do something new!' aspect for much of this year. You might alter your home or change career direction, with solar eclipses in both February and August marking a pivotal time and heralding changes around the family circle too. There may be the patter of tiny feet, possibly long awaited.

A THOUGHT FOR THE YEAR: Everything starts shifting into place at last.

CANCER

JUNE 22 – JULY 22

Your reputation is one of being acutely sensitive to every nuance around you, which makes you an excellent wheeler dealer, often a fine politician, someone who can be tasked and trusted with serious caretaking requirements. That Cancerian crab shell is your way of shielding yourself while you take stock of a situation. You are wary of allowing anyone too close, needing to take your time to get to know folk before allowing them close, but your hospitality is legendary once you open that door, and you're a true nurturer, so you always make sure guests are well fed!

THIS YEAR is a wonderful year to break away from old patterns and to take on something new, perhaps, at work or in terms of dividing your time between two locations, maybe one overseas, as around February in particular, you could be strongly tempted by glorious images of a lovely bolthole. You might also be dividing time between various branches of the family. Jupiter's visit to the lower part of your horoscope will encourage you to feel good about your roots and possibly to extend or improve your home. A relative could benefit from your kindness, wisdom or expertise this year, too.

A THOUGHT FOR THE YEAR: Get ready for a busy time when your popularity will rise!

LEO

JULY 23 – AUGUST 23

The Lion is a proud beast and so are you, although you tend to feel everything acutely, being the utterly wholehearted, committed, loyal and life-embracing person that you are, which means that if life is testing, you really feel it to your core, and when life is fun and fabulous, well, so are you.

Leo draws full-bodied experiences, no half measures for you! You radiate such gorgeous warmth, and despite the fact that Leo is often not the cosiest maternal or paternal sort, somehow as a parent you do get it as right as anyone can.

THIS YEAR brings serious resolutions and plans to improve every corner of your life, with a transformative solar eclipse late in February and another, stronger because it will happen in your sign, Leo, in August. What you start to get yourself clear of earlier in the year seems to pave the way to a fresh chapter which might have been long planned or anticipated.

Your security seems to be enhanced by the autumn, when there may be a business or property transaction underway. Some Leos could be making a long-planned move to a more spacious address, and family ties seem to be stronger by the autumn months, too.

A THOUGHT FOR THE YEAR: Letting go of old clutter allows you to make a fresh start.

VIRGO

AUGUST 24 – SEPTEMBER 22

You have a modest demeanour, yet you can be very lively once you are at ease in company, being ruled by communicator planet Mercury. You have a great appreciation of detail, fully scanning a place or a situation and noting where there's a tweak needed, which isn't to say that Virgo is forever neat and tidy, but you tend to know where everything is, and you are a fiercely independent character, not keen on entrusting your security, happiness or wellbeing into the hands of others, at least until they've proved themselves worthy!

The arts often appeal, as does working with the hands, or with words and there's usually an interest in healthy minds and bodies.

THIS YEAR has a sense of progress around matters material, with significant choices being made this August, concerning your home, or an involvement in the launching of a new enterprise. Jupiter could see the realisation or fruition of an investment of the past, possibly something you've already had earmarked for this year. The autumn months will probably bring your most dynamic and energised phase, with something of a breakthrough that might alter your title or regular routines in a rather surprising, yet beneficial way.

A THOUGHT FOR THE YEAR: Don't be coy about basking in some well-deserved applause.

LIBRA

SEPTEMBER 23 - OCTOBER 23

Justice is so important and you do try to see every angle of a situation, which is why you can appear to be slow to make some decisions. Clued up and in tune with today, you are smooth, gracious, a natural communicator. A lovely host who likes life to be balanced, harmonious and orderly, and to stay connected with your warm circle of friends. However, you are also quite a private person and for all your social skills you actually allow few people really close. You are a master diplomat, great at deflecting overly personal probes, always preferring, endearingly, to ask after others, which increases your popularity, too!

THIS YEAR holds a time of fresh, occasionally out of the blue opportunities to reshape your life and to find paths that allow you to do more of what makes you truly happy and fulfilled, to connect with more like-minded people and, perhaps, to travel further, explore certain parts of the country, of the world that you've been intrigued by but never visited. There could be some interesting invitations flowing your way. Some Librans will be learning new skills or new languages, too. Never count yourself out of something new and exciting. You might be pleasantly surprised.

A THOUGHT FOR THE YEAR: The world's your oyster in this year of opportunity!

SCORPIO

OCTOBER 24 - NOVEMBER 22

You're an all or nothing character who doesn't go in for half measures! You also have a reputation for being secretive, yet you appear quietly approachable, and you'll often find that people choose to confide in you, sensing a depth of understanding that few others will possess.

The infamous 'sting' can be more painful for you than for others, though, as when you hurt, you burn, and you find it hard to move on, needing to understand what happened. You're an amazing, resourceful and loyal friend, and in a crisis, you shine, making you an obvious choice for careers that call for a cool and capable character.

THIS YEAR will be a turning point year for many a Scorpio, when you seem to come into your own, and to start branching out in a new area, possibly more so from the autumn, when opportunity bringing, liberating Jupiter arrives in Scorpio to remind you that you have wings!

There could be financial gains made, with benefits that link to what you might have invested in quite some time ago. Look out for unexpected boosts that add to the bank balance, but also watch for someone's health improvement thanks to a breakthrough.

A THOUGHT FOR THE YEAR: An intriguing new door opens later this summer.

SAGITTARIUS

NOVEMBER 23 – DECEMBER 21

The Sagittarius smile is the first thing we notice. It's dazzling, lighting a room up with a full beam of cheery positivity. You can often cheer yourself up by making others laugh!

Tact and diplomacy can vanish when you are around, as you tell it as you see it, and you can't be doing with swerving this way and that to please others. You have to be true to yourself, with plenty of scope to flex your wings. Sagittarius is depicted by a centaur, who can be a wild, runaway horse or a wise teacher and philosopher. Your heart is kind though and you're at your best when encouraging others.

THIS YEAR Saturn, the great task setter is completing his journey across your own sign by the end of 2017, making this a significant year for you doing something in a stand-alone way, taking command of your direction, possibly after a searching, questing phase that may have seen you giving up some old habits or untying yourself from aspects of the past.

You're standing on your own solid ground this year, and with eclipses marking a fresh start on the home and family front as well as the achievement of a cherished aim, some Sagittarians will be heading up the success ladder at work or reaching retirement with security.

A THOUGHT FOR THE YEAR: Opportunities begin to unfold when you set out your goals.

CAPRICORN

DECEMBER 22 – JANUARY 20

You have a nature that tends to play the long game, investing wisely, as a rule, in people, and knowing the importance of having a good solid network around you. Capricorns often build family empires.

You're a wheeler-dealer with an eye for what's valuable and you often have a sixth sense in business.

Whether you are the ambitious, thrill-seeking mountain goat or the gentler, security conscious, one-step-at-a-time type, you are someone who in early life often seems to have a harder time, and then, as you become more confident and safely self-sufficient, you lighten and sparkle with a youthful air well into your later years.

THIS YEAR sees Saturn, your ruler planet completing a rather karmic journey that began in 2015. One that has seen you letting go of certain associations, old attitudes or perhaps past pain. You have probably been aware of inner shifts and changes, of moments where you've been feeling less like the caterpillar, more like the butterfly you are intended to become.

This is a year for branching out, for family changes that could see your role altering, and for some, it'll be a year when you are called upon to take a bit of a bow, with more appreciation coming for all you've given to others.

A THOUGHT FOR THE YEAR: A liberating moment comes your way in late August.

AQUARIUS

JANUARY 21 – FEBRUARY 18

You're a kind and friendly sort, yet you are also slightly detached, like a spaceman in a suit hovering above the earth, observing humanity. You Aquarians see the straight, logical path that should be taken, but sometimes that isn't so obvious to others, hence the sense of being born ahead of your time. Yes, you can appear bossy as you don't believe in wasting time over explaining what to you is crystal clear! You are secretly shy in a new arena, and your intense need for personal space means you aren't so keen on being fenced into regular social ties unless, of course, there's a hobby or pet passion involved!

THIS YEAR the planet associated most with your sign is Uranus, known for rotating in a strange sideways fashion - a little quirky, like your good self! Uranus makes some concessions this year, aligning positively with Saturn, which is good for merging the old with the new and also for reaching decisions that work well for the longer term for you and yours. You're centre stage in August, when there could be a beneficial financial changeover happening, something afoot that brings added stability and security. Some Aquarians will fulfil a heartfelt wish that seems to have an element of needing to trust and believe in your own capabilities, and to dare to take a certain plunge.

A THOUGHT FOR THE YEAR: Breakthroughs come when least expected, freeing you up.

PISCES

FEBRUARY 19 – MARCH 20

Dreamy, poetic and intuitive, you find pleasure in so many things that others might miss and if ever there was a sign that appreciated kindness, it's yours. Compassion flows through you very easily. You are usually to be found spinning many plates and tend to give way more than you should, sometimes wearing your rosy specs!

Achieving a better balance between the give and take is important, as is valuing yourself, and believing in yourself. Pisces can be a real achiever, and past kindness often comes flying back from a least expected direction, to help make your dreams come true.

THIS YEAR you could be restructuring your life, perhaps, making some changes around commitments at work or getting various financial affairs working better for you or for someone close who could benefit from your experience.

There's a fresh start solar eclipse in late February, marking a chance to begin a new chapter, and a four-month phase where money matters are extra prominent, with some to-ing and fro-ing that could culminate in added security come August, when there could be a significant transaction or an official confirmation that ties various plans up. You could make a surprising gain before this year is over.

A THOUGHT FOR THE YEAR: Lady luck taps your shoulder twice, in her own way.

Spring into

With flowers bursting into bloom and fields full of frolicking lambs, it's the perfect time to get out and about in nature

FAMOUS FOOTSTEPS

Wander 'lonely as a cloud' in search of daffodils just as William Wordsworth once did with a trip to the Lake District. Explore pretty Grasmere and plan a visit to Dove Cottage, where the poet lived from 1799 – 1850. Here you can see an enormous collection of letters, journals, poems and significant objects from his life, as well as popping into the semi-wild garden which is faithful to how the poet kept it.

◆ *Call 01539 435544 or visit http://wordsworth.org.uk*

PIC: ALAMY

Budding artists will find endless inspiration in the Durham Dales. Famous painter JMW Turner returned to the area time and again, and it's easy to see why. Follow in his footsteps through Hamsterley Forest to the stunning High Force waterfall. The area is humming with country pubs too, so there are plenty of nice stop-offs to enjoy. If the weather is less than kind, head to the Bowes Museum instead for its collection of fine and decorative arts including delicate porcelain and an exquisite silver swan musical automaton.

◆ *For more suggestions visit www.thisisdurham.com*

BIRTHDAY BARD

April 26th is Shakespeare's 453rd birthday, and what better way to celebrate than with a trip to his hometown of Stratford-Upon-Avon? There are often special events going on to mark the occasion. You can also catch a play at the glorious RSC theatre, or step into numerous buildings that played a part in the Bard's life and are open for visits.

◆ *Find out more at www.visitstratforduponavon.co.uk*

action

FUN ON THE FARM

It's lambing season! Celebrate all things small and fluffy by popping into Adam Henson's Cotswold Farm Park. The Countryfile favourite has made rare breeds his life's work, and you'll be able to meet creatures with intriguing names - from Castlemilk Moorit sheep, to Kune Kune pigs and Belted Galloway cattle. There's also a special wildlife walk with stunning views across the rolling hills, and information boards to follow. There are sure to be lots of interactive activities available for the grandchildren, just check beforehand.

◆ *Call 01451 850307 or visit www.cotswoldfarmpark.co.uk*

London can be pricey, but there's a little slice of countryside that's free to visit. Mudchute farm, in the middle of the Isle of Dogs. A registered charity, it's open year-round to teach little ones about farming and animals and preserve the local wildlife. Opened by local residents in the Seventies, it's now one of the largest inner city farms in Europe, with more than 100 animals and fowl to see. Meet rare breeds, horses and ponies, or make friends with smaller creatures in Pets' Corner. Guided tours can be organised in advance at a cost. Catch the DLR to Crossharbour station to visit.

◆ *Call 020 7515 5901 or visit www.mudchute.org*

THREE OF THE BEST...

National Trust bluebell sites

Ickworth, Suffolk, is not only a picturesque spot to enjoy the sweet scent of native bluebells, but it also boasts crocus, cyclamen, daffodils, tulips, scilla, chionodoxa and cowslips - a veritable spring carpet of flowers! Afterwards explore the Georgian house, including its servants' quarters, and wander England's earliest Italianate garden.

◆ *www.nationaltrust.org.uk/ickworth*

You'll feel like you've had a holiday after a visit to 'Little Switzerland' - or the grounds of Hardcastle Crags, as it's better known. The Yorkshire woodland got its moniker thanks to its 400 acres of picturesque valleys, pathways and waterfalls, and spring visitors will love its rich bluebell coverage. There are more than 15 miles of pathways to walk, and little ones can amuse themselves by looking for northern hairy wood ants - an unlikely insect that lives in the woodland.

◆ *www.nationaltrust.org.uk/hardcastle-crags*

Castle Ward, County Down, boasts five miles of bluebell trails, bursting with butterflies, to keep even the most energetic explorer occupied. If the weather's less than kind, head inside to admire the 18th century mansion which is famed for its quirky mixture of architectural styles. There's also a barn where would-be farmers can enjoy driving pedal tractors and playing dress up.

◆ *www.nationaltrust.org.uk/castle-ward*

GET YOUR GARDEN OFF TO A
flying start!

Sow hardy annual seed now for a colour-packed garden next year!

Hardy annuals are a real gardener's gift. Colourful, tough, easy to grow and fast to flower, sowing these now will get your garden geared up for a tremendous summer.

Most hardy annuals grow best in full sun and many are fairly low-growing, so earmark some space towards the front of a sunny border for sowing your seed. If you want to create a wild-looking display in a border, mix together lots of packets and sow direct onto the soil to create a higgledy-piggledy but beautiful mix of summer colour.

Once you've got the technique cracked, turn over to find the best hardy annuals for your garden. The choice is bold and beautiful!

You can, of course, also sow hardy annuals in autumn. They're hardy enough to sit out all winter, which means they're in place, ready to start growing as soon as the weather picks up, so you won't have as long to wait for a colourful slice of summer in the flower border.

Need a weekly gardening fix? Then why not try Garden News magazine. Each issue is packed full of practical, down-to-earth gardening tips, grow-your-own advice, ideas and inspiration, as well as information on new plants, products and great money-saving offers.

Carol Klein on sowing annuals

Some of the finer hardy annual seed, such as cornflowers, love-in-a-mist, limnanthes and their ilk can be broadcast sown, chucked up in the air and allowed to grow wherever they land. As they sprout they can be thinned out so they have plenty of elbow room. Bigger seed such as calendula can be station sowed, in other words, pushed lightly into the soil wherever you want them to grow. Remember hardy annuals need plenty of elbow room. Sowing too thickly can mean poor, overcrowded plants but as long as they are thinned out they'll give loads of lively colour.

You can also sow the same seed in autumn. Use seed tray modules, one seed to a compartment, cover with grit, water well and leave in a sheltered place outside. The new plants will grow slowly through the winter and, when they put on their first flush of spring growth, can be planted out in their final positions. Autumn-sown annuals will start to produce their flowers weeks earlier than spring-sown.

STEP-BY-STEP: HOW TO SOW HARDY ANNUALS DIRECT

1 You can sow hardy annuals direct into the ground this month. Choose a sunny patch of the border and make sure the soil isn't stickily wet.

2 Fork over the soil to remove any perennial weeds and all of their roots, plus break down large clods and improve drainage.

3 Next rake it level and to remove any large stones. Keep raking until the soil has broken down to a fine, crumbly texture or 'tilth'.

4 Fill a bottle with sand and use it to mark out areas so you can create blocks or drifts of different kinds of hardy annuals.

5 Make drills within each block and sow the seed thinly into them. The straight lines won't be noticeable once the plants have grown.

6 Rake over the soil to cover the seed and water in, as well as in dry weather. Thin the seedlings out so they have room to develop.

Soap stars

TOP TIP
Soap moulds are sold in craft shops, or you could use silicone cake moulds instead.

YOU WILL NEED

Gloves
Knife
1kg (2¼lb) white melt-and-pour soap bars
Heatproof bowl
Pan
Spatula
Spoon
¼-¾ tsp yellow natural mineral colour
½ tsp dried lemon peel granules
Lemon essential oil
Square mould
Surgical spirit in a spray bottle
9 dried lemon slices
Clingfilm

These beautiful soaps are an easy-to-make handmade gift that everyone will love

1 Wearing gloves, chop the melt-and-pour soap into pieces and heat in a heatproof bowl over a pan of boiling water, stirring occasionally, until all lumps have melted.

3 Add the lemon peel granules a little at a time, stirring gently. Continue stirring until the granules are spread evenly throughout the soap mixture.

5 Pour approximately three quarters of the mixture into the mould. Leave the remainder in the bowl over the hot water to keep it melted and warm.

2 Add the desired amount of colouring to the melted soap base and stir until the powder has mixed in and the colour is evenly distributed.

4 Just before you pour the soap mixture into the mould, slowly add the essential oil and stir gently until it is evenly distributed throughout.

6 Spray the mixture with surgical spirit to remove any bubbles. Leave this first layer for 20-25 minutes until it is almost set. It should be hard but warm.

7 Spray the almost-set layer again with surgical spirit. This will act as a glue and help it to bond to the next layer of soap.

8 Slowly pour the remaining mixture into the mould and add the dried lemon slices. You will need to act fast, as the top layer will begin to set as soon as it is poured in.

9 Create a 3x3 pattern so that each slice of soap will contain a lemon slice. Spritz the surface with surgical spirit to remove any bubbles and leave until hard.

10 Remove the soap from the mould and cut it with a knife into nine even squares. Wrap each square in clingfilm to prevent it attracting moisture.

This project is from The Crafter's Year, published by DK (£14.99, www.dk.com)

IF YOU LIKED THIS TRY THESE...

Juniper cake-slice soap

You will need
1kg (2¼lb) white melt-and-pour soap base
¼ tsp pink natural mineral colour
2½ tsp juniper essential oil
100g (3½oz) juniper berries
A round mould

Made like the lemon soap, but in two stages. First, melt half the soap, adding the pink colour and half the essential oil. Pour it into a round container and let it set, spritzing it with surgical spirit to get rid of any bubbles. Melt the second half of the soap, adding the remaining scent. Spritz the base again, and pour on the second layer of soap. Add the juniper berries to the top, spritzing it one final time to get rid of any remaining bubbles. Once set, remove from the mould and cut into slices.

Moulded vanilla stars

You will need
1kg (2¼lb) white melt-and-pour soap base
¼-¾ tsp cream natural mineral colour
2½ tsp vanilla essential oil
30g (1oz) vanilla pods
Star-shaped moulds

Make in the same way as the lemon soap but pour the mixture into individual moulds to set. Vanilla seeds are used instead of lemon peel granules as an exfoliant and for added scent. Vanilla pods can also be used to decorate the tops of the stars by placing them into the mould before the mixture is poured on top.

Cookie-cutter lavender hearts

You will need
1kg (2¼lb) white melt-and-pour soap base
¼-¾ tsp purple natural mineral colour
2½ tsp lavender essential oil
10g (¼oz) dried lavender

Use the same method as the lemon soap, but swap to the above ingredients. Then instead of cutting the soap into squares, cut with heart-shaped cookie cutters. The lavender buds will float to the top, creating a pretty exfoliating layer.

See-through orange soap

You will need
1kg (2¼lb) clear melt-and-pour soap base
2½ tsp bergamot essential oil
9 dried orange slices

Melt half of the clear soap base, and add half of the essential oil. Pour the mixture into a square mould and add the orange slices to the top. Allow to set before melting the remaining half of the soap base and adding the remaining oil. Spritz the set layer with surgical spirit and add the melted soap mixture to the top. Spritz again to get rid of any bubbles and allow to set. Cut into nine squares.

◆ The melt-and-pour soap base, moulds and mineral colours are available from specialist craft suppliers or online stores such as Amazon or Ebay

Summer fun

PERFECT PICNICS

Mark national picnic week in June with a trip to your local beauty spot. Top Withens (or Withins - no one is certain of the spelling) is an ideal setting for a summer's day. Right in the heart of Brontë country, this hilly wilderness is thought to have inspired the location of the Earnshaw family home in Wuthering Heights. Burn off your sandwiches with a 1¾ mile stroll from Top Withens to the Brontë Waterfall, near Haworth, which is considered to have been one of the sisters' favourite places.

◆ *Discover more walks in the area at www.haworth-village.org.uk. For more picnic inspiration, visit www. nationalpicnicweek.co.uk*

PIC: ALAMY

A TOUCH OF MAGIC

Search for imps, nymphs and other magical folk at the Fairy Pools in Skye. You'll find these clear blue pools at the foot of the Black Cuillins near Glenbrittle, and will understand immediately how they got their name - there's something otherworldly about their beauty. The bold can try a spot of wild swimming, while land-lubbers can satisfy themselves by taking photos.

FLY A KITE

Britain is Europe's windiest country – while this is bad news for those of us with unruly hair, it's great news for kite fans. Make a paper kite (or buy something more elaborate) and take the grandchildren for a day on a hillside. All together now: "Let's go fly a kite..."

◆ Holkham, in Norfolk, offers expanses of sands and an often stiff breeze – plus it's part of England's biggest nature reserve so take your binoculars, too, for some wildlife watching.

◆ Get inspiration for your own designs at Portsmouth International Kite Festival, which has been running (or flying) for 26 years. Features include giant cartoon kites, artistic kite displays set to music, and plenty of children's entertainment. Visit www.portsmouthkitefestival.org.uk to find dates for the 2017 festival.

◆ Coombe Hill is one of the highest points in the Chilterns (as well as being a Site of Scientific Interest for its chalk grassland and wildflowers) and offers amazing views of Aylesbury Vale, as well as perfect kite flying conditions. Take a picnic if it's not too blowy and look out for butterflies including the small heath and ringlet.

◆ While away spare hours in London for free with a kite flying expedition to Hampstead Heath. Climb to the top of Parliament Hill for your best chances, and look out for views of the Shard, St Pancras railway station, Euston Tower and other landmarks.

GO APE

If the warmer weather gets you feeling energetic, why not take the grandchildren for an action-packed day out at a Go Ape woodland? There are numerous sites across England, Scotland and Wales, each offering their own unique treetop adventures, including zip-lines and balance beams – don't worry though, you're safely strapped in at all times. There are mini adventures for little ones too, as long as they're taller than one metre. Not for those with a fear of heights, but if you're feeling brave, a day exploring your inner Tarzan could leave you feeling invincible! Prices start from £18 for children, £33 for adults.

◆ *Call 0333 920 6248 or visit https://goape.co.uk/ to find your nearest centre.*

THREE OF THE BEST...

Sandy beaches

Watergate Bay, Newquay
There's a reason for the continuing popularity of Cornwall's Newquay, and the golden sand of its beaches has something to do with it. There are picturesque cliffs and caves, along with rockpools teeming with life – all of which makes it a paradise for little ones.

Compton Bay, Isle of Wight
This two-mile stretch of contrasting light and dark sands is a top spot for fossil fans – hundreds of fossils lurk inside the chalky cliffs. Walk along the top to see brilliant butterflies, including Adonis blue, dark-green fritillary and Glanville fritillary.

Lunan Bay, Angus
If it's dramatic scenery you're after, it doesn't get better than the sandy dunes and ruined Red Castle of Lunan Bay. It's an unspoilt spot with a magical feel - the cliffs and rocks have a pink sandstone tint. If it rains there's a silver lining too. After a shower the shore will sometimes glitter with semiprecious stones including agate and jasper.

LOVELY LIDO

Keep your cool with a visit to one of the UK's many open-air swimming pools. The Stonehaven Open Air Pool in Aberdeen is fine enough to tempt even the most reluctant of swimmers. It's Olympic-sized and filled with heated, filtered seawater. The pretty Art Deco building alone is worth a visit. It stays opens late during the height of summer for starlit dips.

◆ *For more information call 01569 762134 or visit www.stonehavenopenairpool.co.uk*

Lawn & order!

Want an impeccable lawn? It's the ideal time to get stuck in if so!

After a summer of wear and tear, autumn is the time to replenish your lawn and help it recover. Scarifying, aerating and top-dressing then feeding your lawn will encourage stronger roots, giving you a healthier patch ready for the following year. A little maintenance will also help reduce the risk of waterlogging, compaction and disease through the winter months.

Scarifying, aerating and top dressing improve drainage and encourage grass to grow more strongly, crowding out moss and weeds in the process. Start by mowing to get rid of soft top growth and clear the grass of any fallen leaves and garden debris. Then use a spring-tined rake to remove as much thatch as possible. If thatch - a layer of debris that accumulates at the base of your turf - is allowed to build up, it makes it difficult for water to get through to the grass roots. If you have a very large lawn you could buy an electric rake but otherwise it's probably not worth the expense. Once you've cleared the thatch away, your grass will produce new runners and side shoots to form a dense, thick lawn.

After scarifying, aerate with a garden fork to open up the soil. If your soil is heavy clay try using a hollow tiner rather than a fork, to pull out plugs of soil (it's hard work but worth the effort). Finally, spread a top dressing mixture across the lawn and brush it into the holes. Do this on a dry day so that you don't end up with a muddy lawn! Grass growing on clay soil will benefit from the improved drainage, while lighter soils will be bulked up over time. Use a ready-prepared top-dressing mixture such as Evergreen Enriched Lawn Soil or mix your own using six parts sharp sand, three parts top soil and one part compost (add more sand if your soil is heavy).

Fertilise your lawn with an appropriate feed for the time of year. Autumn feed is high in phosphates to help your grass develop a stronger root system. Whereas spring/summer lawn feed is high in nitrogen to encourage vigorous growth and help prevent weeds and moss from establishing

Take the opportunity to redefine the edges of your lawn too. Chopping into the grass with a half moon edger is much easier during autumn when the ground is damp and easy to 'dig' into.

REPAIRING LAWN DAMAGE

Autumn is the ideal time to tackle patches of lawn that are bare or damaged and to even out any bumps or hollows that have formed. If you have bare patches, the soil will be warm enough for grass seed to germinate in early autumn and the seed is unlikely to dry out, although it may need the occasional watering. Loosen the soil down to a digging fork's depth and break up clods with a rake before you sow the seed on the soil surface. Lightly rake the seed into the soil, then water if the soil is dry and dusty. Cover the sown area with fleece or netting to prevent hungry birds from pecking at it.

Need a weekly gardening fix? Then why not try Garden News magazine. Each issue is packed full of practical, down-to-earth gardening tips, grow-your-own advice, ideas and inspiration, as well as information on new plants, products and great money-saving offers.

STEP-BY-STEP: 3 STEPS TO A BETTER LAWN

1 Scarify with a spring-tined rake. Pull the rake towards you, raking vigorously. The tines of the rake should scratch into the soil surface. Do this in several directions to get as much thatch off the lawn as possible. Put the rakings on the compost heap.

2 Use a garden fork to aerate the lawn. Push it deep into the soil surface and wiggle it backwards and forwards to open up holes, leaving 15cm (6in) gaps between holes. Don't walk over the holes you've already made or it will close them up again.

3 Finish by top-dressing the lawn. This fills in the holes and improves the condition and drainage of your lawn. Do this on a dry day, using a spade to broadcast your top-dressing mixture over the lawn. Brush the mixture into the spiked holes with a besom or broom.

Bags of style

This cool Nordic-inspired bag is pretty and practical – perfect for storing all your essentials

YOU WILL NEED

80x70cm (32x27½in) light blue and white polka-dot cotton fabric for the outer bag

210x8cm (85x3in) of the same fabric for the straps

80x70cm (32x27½in) light blue and white striped lining fabric

25cm (10in) square white cotton fabric

25cm (10in) square lightweight iron-on interfacing

30cm (12in) gray/blue cotton lace, 20mm (¾in) wide

One white plastic button, 18mm diameter

Two white plastic buttons, 22mm diameter

White sewing thread

Wooden spoon

Basic kit including scissors and dressmaker's pins

1 Trace off all the templates (right) and enlarge on a photocopier by 200%. Copy the bag template and cut out two bag panels from the polka-dot fabric.

2 Apply iron-on interfacing to the back of the white cotton fabric and cut out two half-heart shapes, plus eight leaves (four large and four small). To plait the heart 'fingers', start by lifting the left-hand finger over the right-hand finger, then take it under the middle finger and over the left-hand finger. The next finger goes the opposite way and the last finger is plaited like the first. Trim off any edges that stick out. Position the heart in the middle of the front of the bag, 5cm (2in) from the top, with the leaves in pairs underneath. Using white thread, machine stitch the heart to the front of the bag. Sew along both sides of each 'finger' to keep them in place. Sew around each leaf and then down the middle to create the vein.

3 Stitch the cotton lace strip to the top of the front panel, leaving 2-3cm (1in) sticking out each side.

4 Pin the front and back panels right sides together. Machine stitch along the side and bottom edges. Gather the 'cut-out' corners together and lay them flat on top of each other pulling out into a straight line. Sew straight across on both sides of the bag.

5 Turn the bag right side out and push out all corners and seams. Gently iron the bag.

Now make the button strip. From the leftover fabric, cut a strip of polka-dot fabric measuring 8x4cm (3x1½in). Fold over 1cm (⅜in) to the wrong side along each long edge, then fold the strip in half and press again. Machine stitch along the long unfolded side.

6 Use the bag template to cut out two panels of lining fabric. Pin them right sides together and machine stitch the side seams only. Trim all loose threads. Place the outer bag inside the lining tube, with right sides together, and pin together along the top edge.

7 Fold the button strip in half lengthwise. Place it in the centre of the back panel, between the two layers, with the loop pointing downward. Sew all around the opening, sewing over the button strip a few extra times to make sure it's secure.

8 Pull the lining up over the bag, so that both lining and outer bag are right side out, and make sure the button strip is in the right position. Close up the corners at the bottom of the lining, as you did on the outer bag in step 4.

9 Now make the strap. Cut six lengths each 35cm (14in) long - three for each side of the strap. Round off the corners on one end of four of the lengths: in total you will ne round-end strips and t straight mi strips. Taki 1cm (⅜in) s allowance, stitch each middle stri to the straig ends of the two of the rounded strips. Pres: the seams open.

10 Pin the straps right sides together. Using pins, mark a 6cm (2½in) gap along one long side: this is where you will start and stop sewing. Sew all around the strap, then turn it right side out, using the handle of a wooden spoon to help. Press the strap flat, then sew all around it twice, spacing the stitching lines about 6mm (¼in) apart, to make it extra sturdy.

11 Add one small white button to the center front of the bag, stitching it over the lace with white thread. Then add a larger button to each side of the bag. Hold the end of the strap to the side of the bag and sew the button to the bag, stitching through the strap, bag, and lining.

This project is from Sew Scandinavian by Kajsa Kinsella. Photography by Penny Wincer. Published by CICO Books (£12.99, www. rylandpeters.com)

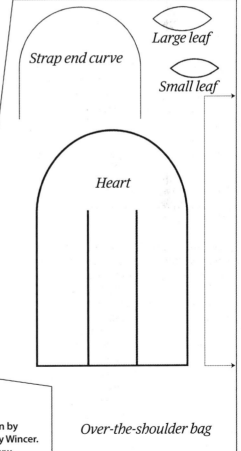

Strap end curve

Large leaf

Small leaf

Heart

Over-the-shoulder bag

Amazing Autumn

BOOKED UP

September 13th is Roald Dahl Day, as it was the author's birthday, so why not celebrate his life and works with a day out that grandchildren will love? The award-winning Roald Dahl Museum, in Buckinghamshire (where he lived for 36 years) is a sweet little attraction aimed at 6-12 year-olds. You'll discover more about his life, writing process and how he was inspired, through interactive exhibitions that are sure to get their imaginations firing.

◆ *For more information call 01494 892192 or visit www.roalddahl.com/museum*

Alternatively, bookworms might prefer a visit to the annual 10-day Jane Austen Festival, which happens each September in her hometown of Bath. Events include workshops, readings, dances and an impressive costumed procession through the town – which won the Guinness World Record for the largest gathering of people dressed in Regency costumes back in 2014.

◆ *For more information and 2017 dates call 01225 443000 or visit www.janeaustenfestivalbath.co.uk*

SWAN ABOUT

There are few sights more spectacular than flocks of swans gliding through a dusky autumn night. To see it for yourself, pay a visit to the Wildfowl and Wetlands Trust's centre at Welney, in the heart of the Fens. While away a few hours watching an afternoon swan feeding (most days from October – March) from a heated hide. You'll see visiting whooper and mute swans, as well as numerous duck species, set against some stunning wintery skies. Admission costs from £7.45 adults, £3.64 children.

◆ *For more information call 01353 860711 or visit www.wwt.org.uk/wetland-centres/welney/*

REMEMBER, REMEMBER...

If you feel like travelling further than your local fireworks display, you won't find better than the annual bonfire celebrations at Lewes, on the south coast. It's always a big affair, with several bonfire societies, marching bands, parades, costumes, 17 burning crosses carried through the town and huge bonfires on the surrounding hills. And that's without mentioning the spectacular fireworks. It gets quite crowded, but it's free to attend. Visit on November 5, of course!

◆ *For more information visit www.lewesbonfirecelebrations.com*

SEAL OF APPROVAL

Is there anything more appealing than a fluffy baby seal? We certainly can't imagine it. Find out for yourself with a trip to Donna Nook National Nature Reserve, on the Lincolnshire coast, where autumn is baby season! Between late October and December grey seals will be hauled up on the sand to give birth to their pups, and a special viewing area is opened up for visitors, designed to minimise any disturbance to the animals. Buy a hot drink from the catering van, take plenty of photos, and prepare for some serious 'ahhhhs'.

◆ *For more information visit www.lincstrust.org.uk/donna-nook*

THREE OF THE BEST...

Woodland walks

Discover one of our least well-known native tree species at Foxley Wood, in Fakenham, Norfolk. The Wild Service tree can be recognised by its jagged leaves (a little like maple leaves) and, in autumn, its bright crimson leaves. You'll also find a strange selection of funghi, plenty of quite and beguiling paths to wander and -if you're lucky - you might hear the twit-twoo of a tawny owl too.

Park your car near Tintern Abbey, Monmothshire, which was made famous through the poetry of Wordsworth, and take a woodland ramble up to the rocky outcrop Devil's Pulpit. Look out for centuries-old oak, yew, birch, beech and ash trees, and you might even see the ultimate autumn spectacle - a deer rut.

Let your imagination run away with you at Glen Finglas, in Stirling. These ancient trees were once the hiding spot for whisky smugglers and deer hunters. It also has links with historical celebrities, as it was a favourite spot of art critic John Ruskin, Pre-Raphaelite painter John Everett Millais and novelist and poet Sir Walter Scott.

◆ *For more woodland routes, visit www.woodlandtrust.org.uk/visiting-woods/*

PAY YOUR RESPECTS

Mark the sacrifices of soldiers by witnessing the National Service of Remembrance at The Cenotaph in Whitehall, on November 12. You don't need a ticket, just stand on the pavements along Whitehall or Parliament Street, which are opened to the public at 8am - arrive early for a good viewing spot. Temporary public toilets can be found in Whitehall Place, and there will be a special area for those in wheelchairs to enable them a better view.

◆ *For more information visit www.britishlegion.org.uk*

Collecting &

Make the most of the perennial plants that present you with free gifts!

From midsummer through to autumn, there are plenty of garden plants starting to produce seed. You can leave most plants alone and let them seed themselves around, but if you have an ordered border and prefer to be a bit more deliberate about it, collect and save that seed, sow it in trays or pots and put the resulting young plants exactly where you want them. The seed will be there, ready and waiting right now, so arm yourself with some paper bags or envelopes and gather as many as you can. Follow these steps to get the best results.

If you like sharing seed with friends, you can get some lovely little posh brown envelopes from mail order companies such as William James & Co (www.wmjames.co.uk) that turn home-saved seed into an incredibly stylish gift! Always collect from healthy looking plants to avoid inadvertently carrying troubles over to your next generation and remember that seed from F1 varieties won't come true to their parent. You can still get some interesting results but it won't necessarily be like the picture on the original packet!

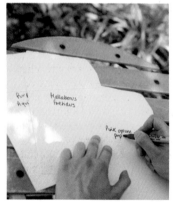

1 Label your envelopes

This might sound obvious, but it saves you a lot of puzzling when you end up with identical looking envelopes with suspicious, unidentified seeds in them! Write the name of what you're collecting on the envelope first and then collect into them.

Need a weekly gardening fix? Then why not try Garden News magazine. Each issue is packed full of practical, down-to-earth gardening tips, grow-your-own advice, ideas and inspiration, as well as information on new plants, products and great money-saving offers.

2 Make sure seed is ripe and ready

For the vast majority of plants, you need to collect the seed when it is ripe. Collect any earlier and the danger is that when you come to sow it, it will not germinate. In most cases, you know when it's ripe because the plant tells you. Shake a poppy's pepper-pot seedhead and when it's ripe the seed rattles inside and comes out of the holes in the top. It's the same with aquilegias and foxgloves. You know they're not ready when the pods are still green and you can't hear the contents rattling.

Other seed pods dry out before releasing ripe seed, such as sweet peas or Californian poppies (eschscholzia), while others pop when the seed is ripe and conditions are right, such as euphorbias (it's best to put a paper bag over their seedheads to catch the seeds before they're explosively released).

Plants such as scabious, amberboa and liatris have seeds that are blown from the seedhead by wind when they're ready. You need to keep a regular eye on your plant to make sure you catch ripe seed at the critical moment, just before the plant disperses itself!

saving seed

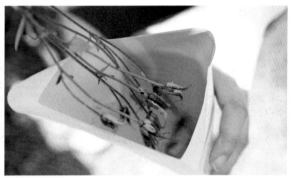

3 Decide what to sow and store

Most seed can be collected and sown straight away, or stored for later sowing, either in autumn or the following spring. In some cases, seed has to be sown immediately, while it is still fresh. Hellebore seed is ripe when squeezing the pods causes them to split and release their seeds. It should be sown there and then and left over winter (the cold weather breaks the seeds' dormancy, a process known as stratification).

Check that seed looks viable before you store it. Viable seed tends to look healthy – shiny and plump. If they appear shrivelled or withered, or the outer seed casing is damaged, there's a chance they may not germinate and spending time storing would be pointless.

4 Store seed correctly

If you're storing seed for later use, it needs to be stored in the right way or you could risk it failing. Breathable paper bags or envelopes are the best; plastic bags can cause seed to 'sweat' and potentially rot. The seed needs to be dry, so leave the seedheads or seed to dry out thoroughly for two or three weeks before putting it into storage. Once they're thoroughly dry, the seeds will also be easier to separate from their seed capsules, seedheads or any other 'chaff', whether that's simply shaking seed from pods, or winnowing it from its casing. You can do this by spreading the seed out on a piece of paper and blowing lightly across it to blow away the lighter debris, leaving the seed behind. Once it's dried, cleaned and safely in its paper bags or envelopes, put it in a cool, dry place out of direct sunlight, where the temperature remains pretty constant - definitely not the greenhouse!

GOOD PLANTS TO COLLECT SEED FROM

Aquilegias	Lathyrus vernus	Honesty	Primroses	Sweet cicely
Wait until pods are brown. It may take until August. They appear in lots of colours so be selective and save seed from your favourites.	Ping open the dark, slender pods to reveal the seed inside and sow next spring after soaking in cold water overnight.	Wait until late summer or autumn then rub away the outer layer of the flat disc with your hands to reveal the silvery inside and the seeds.	An exception to the rule, primrose seed is best collected and sown while it's 'green' in the summer to prevent the seed going dormant.	Can be sown when 'green', or when ripe, but it will then need vernalisation (a cold period) to break down germination inhibitors.

Coffee-filter

This unusual project is surprisingly easy and gives beautiful results

YOU WILL NEED

130 coffee filters

15-20cm (6-8in) in diameter (including 10 bleached/white filters)

Food coloring: pink, orange & green

Tea bags

5 bowls or pots for mixing dyes

Rubber gloves

1.2m (4ft) length of foam pipe insulation (available from diy stores)

Scissors

Duct tape

Several sheets of neutral tissue paper

PVA glue

Masking tape

Stapler

Hot glue gun

1 Prepare your five dyes: light pink, dark pink, orange, brown, and green. For the two pink dyes, orange, and green, add a few drops of food coloring to a small bowl of water – add more drops for the darker pink. For the brown dye, add two or three tea bags to a small bowl of boiling water. Let cool and remove the tea bags before using.

2 Set aside the 10 bleached filters, then divide up the rest into 70 for pink, 40 for neutrals, and 10 for greens. Wearing rubber gloves to protect your hands, dip your filters into your mixes so that they are submerged and will absorb the colors. Wring them out and then peg them onto a line or lay them over radiators to dry (use an old tea-towel to protect any surfaces from the dye). This will take a few hours.

3 In the meantime, the wreath base can be made. Use scissors to cut two rectangles of foam away from one end of the pipe. Cut corresponding pieces from the other end, so that the two ends will fit together in a sort of dovetail join. Place the two ends of the pipe together and tape securely with duct tape.

wreath

4 Tear up enough strips of tissue paper to completely cover the wreath base and paste to the wreath base using PVA glue. Leave to dry - this could take up to four hours, but you can speed up the process with a hairdryer.

5 When your filters are dry, start making the ruffled flowers: Stack five filters on top of each other (three dark and two light), and then fold them into quarters.

6 Use scissors to cut scalloped or pointed petals into the ends. Staple the fold at the base to secure.

7 Holding the stapled end, open out the layers, but as you do this, pinch and twist the base of the flower; this will create a very pretty ruffled flower. When all the layers are fluffed out, tape the base of the flower with masking tape to hold it in place until it is glued to the wreath. Repeat to create nine flowers like this, using a mix of pink, brown, and white filters.

8 To make the taped flower: make a stack of three filters (use graduated colors or a mix) and fold into quarters. Cut a scalloped edge along the top and then cut out the center, again with a scalloped edge. Set the outer pieces aside to use in step 9. Repeat to make about 20-30 flower centers, depending on how full you want your wreath to look.

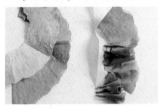

9 Twist each flower center piece at the base to create a petal and press two or three of these on to a strip of masking tape about 25cm (10in) long. Then take the reserved outer pieces and almost pleat these as you stick them down, creating a long ruffle on the tape.

10 Take your ruffled strip and start to roll the tape, starting where the centre petals are. This will create a very pretty but shallow ruffled rose.

11 Repeat to make 10-15 of these flowers.

12 To make the leaves, cut six or seven spiky leaf shapes from each green filter. These leaves will be glued into your wreath while you are attaching the flowers to the base.

13 Now start attaching your flowers - a hot glue gun is essential here. Think about how you would like the composition to look; you could cluster the larger flowers together to create an asymmetric display or go haphazard and literally 'pick and stick'! Use the smaller flowers around the larger ones and fill in the gaps with the leaves.

This project is from Paper Pom-poms & Other Party Decorations by Juliet Carr. Photography by Holly Joliffe & Emma Mitchell. Published by CICO Books (£12.99, www.rylandpeters.com)

Winter wonderlands

Cold weather is no excuse for being a recluse. Reap the benefits of getting out and about in these beautiful spots

COASTAL ESCAPES

The Isles of Scilly are Britain's warmest spot, with average temperatures in January hovering around 7°C – higher than winter temperatures in Nice! Get bundled up for a windswept walk along the white sands, or take in a visit to the Abbey Garden which is home to around 200 plant species. If you're visiting over the festive season, you can even help the islanders with their annual plant stock take on New Year's Day.

If it's Vitamin D you're after, head to Eastbourne, which boasts an average five hours and 23 minutes of sunshine per day, adding up to 1,962 hours across the year. Make sure to include a visit to Battle Abbey where you can stand on the site where Britain's future was forged – the battlefield of the famous 1066 Battle of Hastings. Follow in the footsteps of King Harold and William the Conqueror, learn more in the visitor centre and enjoy a re-enactment of events (available on specific dates).
◆ To find out more call 0370 333 1181 or visit www. english-heritage.org.uk

Blow away the cobwebs (and burn off those mince pies) with a trek along the Wales Coast Path, which runs along almost the entire Welsh coast. In Swansea Bay you can walk more than 400 miles of public rights of way, including the town's highest point at Penlle'r Castell where you're in for spectacular views.
◆ *For more information and available routes, see www.visitswanseabay.com*

KEEP COSY

What better way to warm up than with a visit to a natural spa? Soothe away aches and pains with a trip to the historic city of Bath, which has now opened its natural thermal spa baths to the public. The steamy rooftop pool is popular year-round thanks to its stunning views over the city – just as enjoyable in the twinkling evening lights as during the daytime. The mineral-rich warm water is enhanced with bubbling jets, for a real sense of luxury. You can also relax inside in a steam room, perfect for warding off colds. Prices vary, starting at £34pp for two hours.

◆ *To find out more call 01225 331234 or visit www. thermaebathspa.com*

Take shelter from the elements in the glass biomes at Cornwall's Eden Project. This incredible site offers everything a garden-lover could want, and is also excellent for teaching grandchildren about the wider world. Explore the rainforest walkways, looking out for exotically named plants from sausage trees to red stinkwood, and get an insight into how scientists work in an aerial laboratory – it's all inside what is essentially a giant greenhouse, so you can be sure of a toasty warm day out! Prices start from £22.50 per adult, £12.60 for children, when booked in advance.

◆ *To find out more call 01726 811911 or visit www. edenproject.com*

THREE OF THE BEST...

Christmas markets

Lincoln

It's always bustling, but with good reason – it's nestled in the quaint and picturesque castle grounds. Wander the cobbled streets and browse 250 stalls, with a mulled wine in hand. This is the oldest market in England and has a German feel to it, perhaps a result of the town's twinning with Neustadt. Take a break from shopping to burn off a mince pie or two on the town's outdoor ice-skating rink.

◆ *For dates see www.visitlincoln.com*

Windsor

Pick up handmade soaps, jewellery, ceramics, glass, fudge and more at the Windsor Christmas Gift Fair. Held at the famous Royal Windsor Racecourse, this family-friendly event will be crammed with unique gifts from artisan designers and makers, as well as yummy gourmet food and drinks, festive music and plenty of toys and children's clothes to fill those stockings.

◆ *Visit www.windsorchristmasgiftfair.co.uk*

Edinburgh

When it comes to festive magic, nowhere does it quite like the Scottish capital. There are weeks of activities, one highlight of which is the annual market. As well as the usual food and gift stalls, there's an outdoor skating rink in Princes Street Gardens, and a host of charming fairground rides. Seeing the city from the top of a big wheel is not to be missed.

◆ *For dates see www.visitscotland.com*

How to force

Grow scented blooms in time for Christmas!

Scented hyacinths in the house are a must for many of us during winter. Not only are they associated with Christmas festivities, they're also a lovely treat in the depths of winter's dark days, a beautiful precursor of spring. And then there's their heavenly scent, which fills a room far better than an artificial air freshener.

Garden centres have the specially prepared bulbs in stock in the autumn, usually from September. These bulbs have been heat treated so you can force them into flower early in December, rather than their normal spring flowering time. There's a good range of colours available, from traditional blue, white and pink, to more unusual shades of maroon,

peach and yellow.

Most prepared hyacinths need ten weeks growing somewhere cool and dark followed by about three weeks indoors in the light before they'll flower. So if you want them in flower on Christmas Day, aim to have them potted up by the last week of September.

If your skin's sensitive, wear gloves when handling hyacinth bulbs because they can cause skin irritation. Use plastic pots with drainage holes, which can be dropped into decorative pot covers to bring into the house. You can also buy shallow bulb bowls but these often don't have drainage holes so you'll need to tip them on to their sides after watering to let any excess drain away. Or use glass hyacinth vases, where the roots just sit in water.

How to pot them up

To pot up your bulbs, use bulb fibre or soil-based compost and sit the bulbs on top, close together, but not touching. Cover with more bulb fibre but leave the tips of the bulbs exposed. Water and then stand the pots somewhere cool and dark (a cupboard under the stairs, or they could go in a box under the greenhouse staging or in the garage). Check every week or so and give them a tiny bit of water if the compost has dried out completely.

After their ten weeks in the dark, they'll be well rooted and shoots should have appeared. They'll be yellow because of being in the dark, so when

hyacinths

they're about 4-5cm (1½-2in) long, bring them into a cool room in the house where they'll green up, and once that's happened, put them somewhere warmer to grow on and flower.

When they're in flower

To help the flowers last as long as possible, avoid keeping your bulbs too near to radiators or standing them in a draught. If their leaves start to develop faster than their flower buds, move them back to a cooler position and keep them in the dark again for a couple of days, then bring them back out.

Sometimes the flower spikes can get top heavy, if they're fully loaded with those large, fragrant petals. They may need a discreet stake to stop them from flopping over. Use a thin green split cane and gently push it in behind the flower spike - its florets may keep it in place, or use string - but avoid poking the cane into the bulb itself.

Once the flowers have faded, deadhead them by cutting them off as low down as you can. The leaves will start to turn yellow. You can plant them out in the garden at this stage. They'll have been weakened by the forcing process but will revive after a year or so in the ground and flower again. Choose a sunny, well-drained spot and plant the bulbs at two and a half times their depth, trimming their long roots away if needed. They'll revert to their normal flowering time: mid to late spring.

'Paper White' narcissus

'Paper White' daffodils grow more quickly than hyacinths so you can wait until mid-November before planting them up for Christmas flowers. Their dainty white flowers, on long, elegant stalks, have an unusual musky scent, which some people love and others loathe. If you like it, they're very easy to grow. Simply pot up the bulbs, which may already have shoots, in multi-purpose compost, with their tips just below the surface. Water after planting and when the compost feels dry and keep them on a warm sunny windowsill. Put in a few twiggy sticks to support the stems and that's all there is to it.

Need a weekly gardening fix? Then why not try Garden News magazine. Each issue is packed full of practical, down-to-earth gardening tips, grow-your-own advice, ideas and inspiration, as well as information on new plants, products and great money-saving offers.

STEP-BY-STEP: GROWING FORCED HYACINTH BULBS

1 Place the bulbs on a layer of compost, making sure they aren't touching. They should have their tops just showing at the compost surface.

2 Keep the potted-up bulbs somewhere cool (10°C/50°F is warm enough) and dark. Check the compost every few days to make sure it doesn't dry out.

3 When the bulbs have produced 10cm (4in) tall shoots, move them to a well-lit warm room. They should flower in two to three weeks.

Countdown

Who says advent calendars are just for the grandchildren? Fill yours with sweet treats, herbal tea bags, ideas for days out – anything you fancy!

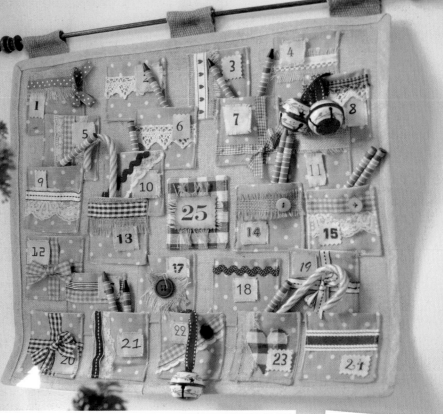

TOP TIP APPLYING BIAS TAPE

Open up the tape and pin right sides together to the edge of the project. Sew along the creased line, taking out the pins as you go. When you meet the start of the tape, overlap by about 0.5cm (¼in). Fold the tape over the edge to the wrong side of your work, pin to the back, then slip stitch to secure.

YOU WILL NEED

46x51cm (18x20in) piece of lightweight burlap/hessian

46x51cm (18x20in) piece of stiff fusible fabric stabiliser

46x51cm (18x20in) backing fabric

24 squares of linen-effect fabric measuring 9cm (3½in) square

One piece of red gingham fabric measuring 9cm (3½in) square

25 pieces of calico or similar measuring 9cm (3½in) square for the back of the pockets

One sheet of printable canvas

1.85m (2 yards) of 2.5cm (1in) bias binding

A selection of ribbon, lace and buttons to decorate

Three pieces of medium-weight burlap/hessian tape measuring 13cm (5in) each

Repositionable spray fabric adhesive

Fabric glue

Pinking shears

Pole for hanging

This project is from Half Yard Christmas by Debbie Shore. Published by Search Press (£10.99, www.searchpress.com)

to Christmas

1 After cutting the 24 square pocket pieces, the first thing to do is decorate them. I sewed strips of ribbon or lace - or both - to the front of each, making each square different. Add buttons and bows as well if you wish!

2 Place each piece, including the red gingham square, right sides together with a calico square and sew around three sides, leaving the bottom edge open.

3 Snip away the excess fabric at the corners to reduce the seam bulk and turn the right way out. Fold the raw edges inwards and press into place.

TOP TIP
It's best to cut your backing fabric too large then trim it to size, to make sure there's enough room to arrange your pockets.

4 To create the numbers for the pockets, use a computer and printer to print numbers 1–25 on to printable canvas, using different fonts available. Make the number '25' larger than the rest.

5 Press with a hot iron to make the ink permanent. Cut out each number, and fray or trim the edges with pinking shears.

6 To give the numbers an aged look, paint them with diluted black tea or coffee.

7 To make the number '25' stand out, shade the edges with an ink pad. Fray a square of burlap/hessian and glue this behind the number.

8 Arrange the pockets on the lightweight burlap/hessian. Placing them randomly and overlapping them slightly disguises any pockets that aren't perfectly square, but don't overlap them so much that you won't be able to put a gift inside. Place the number 25 right in the centre, with no pockets overlapping it.

9 When you're happy with the arrangement, pin each pocket in place then carefully sew around three sides, leaving the top of each pocket open. Reverse a couple of stitches at the start and end of your stitches to strengthen the top of the pockets. Start with the top pockets and work your way carefully downwards. Glue the numbers in place on their pockets.

10 Using the repositionable spray adhesive, place the calendar on top of the backing fabric. Sew the bias tape all the way around. Although, as the back of the calendar is unlikely to be seen, you could glue the bias binding to the back of the calendar instead of hand sewing it.

11 Fold the lengths of burlap/hessian tape in half to create loops and pin them, evenly spaced, across the back of the calendar. Sew them in place.

12 Thread a pole through your burlap/hessian loops and fill all the pockets with presents!

Notable dates for 2017

New Year's Day (Bank Holiday observed)	Monday January 2
Bank Holiday (Scotland)	Tuesday January 3
Epiphany	Friday January 6
Burns' Night	Wednesday January 25
Chinese New Year (Rooster)	Saturday January 28
Shrove Tuesday (Pancake Day)	Tuesday February 28
Ash Wednesday	Wednesday March 1
Valentine's Day	Tuesday February 14
St David's Day	Wednesday March 1
Commonwealth Day	Monday March 13
St Patrick's Day (Bank Holiday N. Ireland/Eire)	Friday March 17
Mothering Sunday	Sunday March 26
British Summer Time begins (clocks go forward)	Sunday March 26
Palm Sunday	Sunday April 9
First Day of Passover (Jewish Holiday)	Monday April 10
Maundy Thursday	Thursday April 13
Good Friday (Bank Holiday)	Friday April 14
Easter Sunday	Sunday April 16
Easter Monday (Bank Holiday)	Monday April 17
St George's Day	Sunday April 23
May Day (Early May Bank Holiday)	Monday May 1
Ascension Day	Thursday May 25
First Day of Ramadan (Islam)	Saturday May 27
Spring Bank Holiday	Monday May 29
Fathers' Day	Sunday June 18
Summer Solstice (Longest day)	Wednesday June 21
Armed Forces Day	Saturday June 24
American Independence Day	Tuesday July 4
Battle of the Boyne (Holiday N. Ireland)	Wednesday July 12
St Swithun's Day	Saturday July 15
Summer Bank Holiday (Scotland / Eire)	Monday August 7
Summer Bank Holiday	Monday August 28
Islamic New Year	Wednesday September 20
Jewish New Year (Rosh Hashanah)	Thursday September 21
Diwali (Hindu Festival)	Thursday October 19
Trafalgar Day	Saturday October 21
British Summer Time ends (clocks go back)	Sunday October 29
Hallowe'en	Tuesday October 31
All Saints' Day	Wednesday November 1
Guy Fawkes' Night	Sunday November 5
Remembrance Sunday	Sunday November 12
St Andrew's Day	Thursday November 30
First Sunday in Advent	Sunday December 3
Winter Solstice (Shortest day)	Thursday December 21
CHRISTMAS DAY	Monday December 25
BOXING DAY	Tuesday December 26
New Year's Eve/Hogmanay	Sunday December 31

DIARY 2017

26 MONDAY

27 TUESDAY

28 WEDNESDAY

29 THURSDAY

30 FRIDAY

31 SATURDAY

1 SUNDAY

Blast from the past

Childhood winters

We lived in a maisonette above the shoe shop in Ruislip Manor where my father was the manager.

There were coal fires in the downstairs rooms and bedrooms and only a metal fire-escape staircase outside to use when carting coal into the house. I remember single-glazed metal-framed windows where the frost flowers formed on the inside in my bedroom, together with great chunks of ice in the corners. The greyness of the light filtering through the curtains, when it had snowed, meant it wasn't necessary to look outside to know that there had been a fall during the night. And there was a distinct difference in the bedroom air that also heralded the fluffy whiteness outside. The kapok filling in the mattress and pillows back then swiftly became lumpy and less comfortable than sleeping on the floor. And we put coats on the bed because the rough old blankets didn't trap air like duvets and however many were piled up they refused to warm the sleeper.

The oil stove in the bathroom fell over and covered the room in a black oily soot deposit and the smell lingered for an age. The damp stain on my bedroom ceiling, where pipes had burst at one time, always looked like a tree to me. One year, my father attempted to unfreeze outdoor pipes by applying burning rags in an old paint tin. Given that he was very, very high up on a massive extending ladder and wearing wellies this was hardly safe!

Sue Bourne, Stoke on Trent

Animal magic

Squirrels have 'senior moments' too, and it's good news for woodlands. It turns out that absent-minded squirrels accidentally plant thousands of new oak trees every year by forgetting where they buried their acorns.

Top tip

Christmas may only just have passed, but this is the perfect time to start thinking about next year's festivities. Look out for bargain wrapping paper, gift tags and Christmas decorations in the winter sales and get stocked up ready for Christmas 2018, all for a fraction of the price you'd pay later on.

Brain teaser

Fill in the squares so that every row, column and each of the nine 3x3 squares contain all the digits from one to nine.

		2			9			
	7		3	5				4
4				6	1	5	9	
		8	6					3
	4	5			7	2	1	
2				3		9		
9	6	4	2				8	
5				9	8			
			4			7		

Answers to all Brain teasers on pages 180 to 182

My perfect pet

NAME: **Angel**
AGE: **3 months**
OWNER: **Sue Farrow**
PET LIKES: **Racing around the room in her ball and eating**
PET HATES: **Loud noises!**
HUMAN TRAITS: **She loves to watch television while sitting on the sofa**

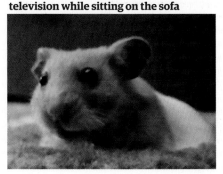

Recipe of the week

VEGETABLE LASAGNE

Serves: 4
Preparation time: 30 mins
Cooking time: 1 hr 30 mins

1 large onion, cut into wedges
2 red peppers, sliced
2 courgettes, sliced
1 aubergine, sliced
100g (3½oz) mushrooms, sliced
2 garlic cloves, peeled and chopped
4 tbsp olive oil
250g (9oz) cherry tomatoes
2 tbsp soy sauce/teriyaki marinade
2 tbsp tomato purée
6-8 sheets of lasagne
600ml (1pt) cheese sauce
2 tbsp each grated cheddar and dry breadcrumbs
Fresh basil leaves to garnish

1 Preheat the oven to 200°C/400°F/Gas Mark 6. Put the onion, peppers, courgettes, aubergine, mushrooms and garlic in a baking dish, drizzle with oil and roast for 30 mins, turning them occasionally. Add the tomatoes and roast for a further 15-20 mins or until the vegetables crisp up at the edges.

2 Mix the honey, garlic and sauce and tomato purée and stir into the vegetables. Spoon half into a large, rectangular dish. Cover with half the lasagne sheets and half the cheese sauce.

3 Layer the remaining vegetables, pasta and cheese sauce on top and scatter over the cheese and breadcrumbs. Bake for 40 mins or until golden and bubbling. Garnish with fresh basil to serve.
Credit: Kikkoman

2 MONDAY

3 TUESDAY

4 WEDNESDAY

5 THURSDAY

6 FRIDAY

7 SATURDAY

8 SUNDAY

My very naughty cat

Holly the cat simply sidled into our lives one day many years ago and caused us a few scares by her antics. But her worst mishap was in January one year. She hadn't returned home by bedtime and so began a very anxious time, with us looking for her in every spare minute we had. But as days went by, we started to believe we would never see her again. We put notices in our local shops and took phone calls from various people sure they'd seen Holly around the area - but to no avail. And then, 18 days later, a lady phoned to say she was sure Holly was sleeping on her car bonnet at night! Having assured her that Holly would come if called, I then got a call from her to say that she was in the lady's house. What joy!

Although rather scruffy and thin, Holly was fine. So I wrote a letter to our local newspaper to thank everyone for their help in looking for her. I was told that a photographer would be calling later that day to take a photo to go with my letter. A small van drew up, I asked the man where he would like us to pose to have our photo taken. He replied that he'd never had an offer like that before as he was only meant to read our gas meter!

Ten minutes later the actual photographer arrived and once he'd stopped laughing at what had just happened, our photograph was taken. Needless to say, Holly's evening activities were curtailed after that stressful time and she lived to swish her tail for a few years after that.

Wilma Hart, Dundee

Top tip

Baby it's cold outside! But while it might be tempting to batten down the hatches, dive under the covers and whack up the thermostat, that could end up pretty costly for your gas bill. Instead try to keep your thermostat at a constant 18-21°C or lower. Notching it up even 1°C higher than that could cost up to £60 a year extra.

Brain teaser

Solve the clues, to find three nine-letter words in the grid below moving from letter to letter either up, down, sideways or diagonally.
1 **Significant event in life or history**
2 **Tourist**
3 **Naive fool**

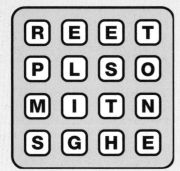

My perfect pet

NAME: **Kali**
AGE: **7**
OWNER: **Lyn Orrick**
PET LIKES: **Her toys, lazing in the window on sunny days and playing outside in the garden**
PET HATES: **Wind and rain**
HUMAN TRAITS: **She's very vocal and loves attention – but only on her terms**

Recipe of the week

OAT SMOOTHIE

Serves: 1
Preparation time: 2 mins

20g (¾oz) porridge oats
25g (1oz) cashew nuts
55ml (2floz) natural yogurt
1 ripe banana, peeled
100ml (3½floz) cold milk
1 tbsp Lyle's Golden Syrup
½ tsp vanilla extract or vanilla bean paste

1 Chop up the banana into thin slices and set aside. Break up the cashew nuts by putting them in a sandwich bag and smashing them with a rolling pin - or place them in a food processer and blitz until they're broken and powdery.

2 Add all of the oats, nuts, banana, milk, yogurt, golden syrup and vanilla paste into a smoothie mixer or blender. Depending on the power of your blender, blend all the ingredients together for 2 mins or until all the nuts and oats have broken down and the mixture has become smooth and less bity. Blitz for longer if the nuts need to break down further. Pour the mixture into a glass and enjoy straight away or keep the smoothie chilled until you want to drink it.

Credit: Lyles Golden Syrup

9 MONDAY

10 TUESDAY

11 WEDNESDAY

12 THURSDAY

13 FRIDAY

14 SATURDAY

15 SUNDAY

Waste not...

I have vivid memories of using a manual typewriter in my first ever job as a naive shorthand typist at the age of 16 in 1961. I worked for an accountant on the top floor of a very old building in Doncaster. Scrooge's hapless clerk, Bob Cratchit, and I had a lot in common when it came to our employers! Not only was the manual typewriter ancient and difficult to use, but when the carbon paper became used, I was made to hold the carbon sheets in front of the gas fire, so that any remaining ink would run down the sheet and it could be used for much longer. The accountant would also never buy new envelopes, and instead bought economy war labels which were stuck on used envelopes after the new addresses had been typed on. He also used to go to the local market and get free potato baskets which were then used for waste paper baskets. I used to have to ask permission to light the gas fire in my office, and he wasn't best pleased when, one day, I lit the fire, threw the match into the potato basket and it caught fire. My wages were £3.5s 0d a week and I was given a five shilling rise when I agreed to do the books for a local coal merchant in addition. How things are different in the modern offices of today!
Patricia Asquith-Dugdale, Leeds

Top tip

If you're over 60 and entitled to free prescriptions, you may also be able to get free non-prescription medicines and treatments through the NHS Minor Ailments Service. This could save you £££s on treatment for common niggles such as coughs, eczema and stomach complaints. Even if you're not entitled to free prescriptions, the scheme allows you to buy these products for much less than the normal price. Find out if the service is available in your area by speaking to your pharmacist.

Animal magic

The English language is incredibly creative when it comes to collective nouns. Our favourites include: a bloat of hippopotamuses; a shrewdness of apes; a business of ferrets and a skulk of foxes.

Brain teaser

In this puzzle, each symbol stands for a whole number between one and nine. The number at the end of each row and column equals the sum of the numbers in it. When a symbol appears twice in a square it is doubled. Can you work out which number each symbol represents?

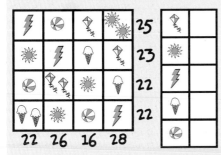

Recipe of the week

RICE PUDDING

Serves: 4
Preparation time: 5 mins
Cooking time: 30 mins

850ml (1½pt) milk/Alpro soya alternative
140g (5oz) short grain pudding rice
100g (3½oz) golden caster sugar
2 eggs
Freshly grated nutmeg, to serve

1 First add the rice and milk to a pan, heating until the mixture just begins to boil. Then reduce the temperature and simmer for around 20-25 mins, until the rice is cooked through. Take a grain out of the pan to test.

2 Lightly whisk the sugar and the eggs in a bowl. Add in a spoonful of the cooked rice and stir vigorously until the rice and the egg mixture are fully combined.

3 Add the rice mixture back to the pan and continue heating for a further 10 mins, until it thickens (it is important to make sure the rice pudding does not boil, as it can curdle). Take the pan off the heat and spoon the mixture into four individual bowls.

4 Grate some fresh nutmeg over the rice pudding to taste, sprinkle over a little more caster sugar on top or add in some spiced fruit compote.
Credit: Alpro

My perfect pet

NAME: **Tessa**
AGE: **5**
OWNER: **Margaret Didcote**
PET LIKES: **Rich tea biscuits, people and muddy puddles**
PET HATES: **Fireworks and being alone**
HUMAN TRAITS: **She looks very guilty if she's done something wrong and smiles whenever she's excited**

16 MONDAY

17 TUESDAY

18 WEDNESDAY

19 THURSDAY

20 FRIDAY

21 SATURDAY

22 SUNDAY

Duty before fashion

In the late Fifties and early Sixties net petticoats with many layers were the height of fashion. As luck would have it, our school summer uniform was a full-skirted dress and in 1961 my mother bought me a very gathered net petticoat which she allowed me to wear to school under my uniform dress. The petticoat was so full that my skirt stuck out almost like a crinoline, I felt fantastic though. Looking back, with all that fabric how on earth did I manage to sit at the old-fashioned, all-in-one desks that we had then?

In winter we wore a blouse and skirt and, when mini-skirts came into fashion a couple of years later, we rolled over the waistband. The higher the mini-skirt hemlines rose in the fashion photos in our favourite magazines, the more times we rolled over our waistbands! And the trendy black stockings of the previous winter gave way to tights (or pantyhose as they were called originally) in American tan because, let's face it, who wanted to show off the tops of their stockings?

The only uniforms we didn't try to make more fashionable were our Girl Guide uniforms. This is a picture of my friend, Pat and me on the day that Lady Baden-Powell, the World Chief Guide at that time, came to Exeter to meet all the Brownies, Guides and Rangers at the cathedral. No black stockings or modern tights here - we are in our short white ankle socks and looking very modest.
Mary Smith, Beds

Top tip

Draughts are a real nuisance at this time of year, in the battle to keep the house warm and cosy. And that's not to mention the draining effect they have on your energy bill. Show them who's boss by filling any gaps around window frames, door frames and any pipes that pass through external walls with draught-excluder strips or expanding foam fillers. Buy or make some draught excluders to place around draughty doors, too.

Animal magic

Horseflies may not be the most impressive of creatures, but they can certainly hold a tune. The insects always hum in the key of F - listen out for it next time there's one trapped in your curtains.

Brain teaser

By entering single-digit numbers into the empty spaces of the grid, can you make the figures in each of the 16 hexagons add up to 30? No two numbers in the same hexagon may be the same and nought cannot be used. We've given you some starter numbers to get you under way.

My perfect pet

NAME: **Beau**
AGE: **2**
OWNER: **Aimee Seward**
PET LIKES: **Balls, long walks, cuddles, peanut butter and swimming in the sea**
PET HATES: **Fireworks, being clean and not being allowed on the sofa when covered in mud**
HUMAN TRAITS: **Sitting at the table when having her tea and sleeping on the bed**

Recipe of the week

CHICKEN STIR-FRY

Serves: 4
Preparation time: 5 mins
Cooking time: 10 mins

3 tbsp honey
1 large orange, zested and juiced
2 tbsp sweet chilli sauce
2 tbsp soy sauce
1 tbsp cornflour
1 tbsp vegetable oil
50g (2oz) cashew nuts
400g (14oz) chicken stir-fry strips
500g (1lb2oz) fresh or frozen stir-fry vegetables
Salt and freshly ground black pepper
Chopped fresh coriander, to garnish

1 Mix together honey, orange zest, orange juice, chilli sauce, soy sauce and cornflour, blending until smooth. Set aside.

2 Heat 1 tbsp oil in a wok or large frying pan and add the cashew nuts, stir-frying them for 1-2 mins until golden. Remove with a slotted spoon and set to one side. Wipe out the wok or pan with kitchen paper.

3 Heat the remaining oil in the wok or frying pan and add the chicken, stir-frying it for 4-5 mins. Add vegetables and stir-fry for another 3-4 mins, until they are cooked, yet still crunchy. Season with salt and pepper.

4 Stir the honey mixture, then add it to the wok, cooking it for 1 min or until thickened. Serve the stir-fry in warmed bowls, sprinkled with the cashew nuts and chopped fresh coriander.
Credit: Rowse Honey

23 MONDAY

24 TUESDAY

25 WEDNESDAY

26 THURSDAY

27 FRIDAY

28 SATURDAY

29 SUNDAY

My earliest memory

Although I was born in hospital as my mother was aged 39 when she had me and I was her first baby, I will never forget the birth of my youngest brother Allan. He was born at home, which was much more common then. My grandparents lived next-door but one, and as my grandmother, sadly, had to have both her legs amputated because she was diabetic, she had a bed downstairs in the living room - and that's where my mother gave birth. I was woken by my father on November 17, 1954 to be told I had a new baby brother and he was taking me to see him. Although I was only two years and eight months, I can still recall vividly the wallpaper in my bedroom - which had been newly decorated with a pretty jonquil and lilac pattern.

When we got to my grandparents, my mother was sitting up in the large double bed - it always seemed large to me, anyway - and the midwife was bathing Allan at the end of the bed in a baby bath before wrapping him up and handing him back to my mother.

This is my earliest memory but I ended up spending a lot of time in that double bed as my grandmother, who sadly died when I was only eight, taught me to crochet when I was about six years old.

Mrs J Mitchell-Smith, Halifax, W Yorks

Top tip

Lined curtains are a great way to block out the winter cold from your home and keep your fuel bills down. And provided you've got a sewing machine, making your own can save you even more money since made-to-measure curtains can be pricey. Look in your local haberdashery for some thermal blackout lining and speak to the sales assistant if you're unsure how to put them together.

Animal magic

Rudolph the Blue-Eyed Reindeer might not be the catchiest song title, but it would be more accurate than a red nose. During the winter reindeers' eyes turn blue to help them see in the lower light.

Brain teaser

Fill in the squares so that every row, column and each of the nine 3x3 squares contain all the digits from one to nine.

1	9							8
		7	4		5	6		2
	2		9				4	
			4		7	8		
		7		3				
	1	3		2				
	7				4		6	
5		6	2		1	3		
3						2	1	

My perfect pet

NAME: **Kovu**
AGE: **9**
OWNER: **Jade Baldwin and Jane Sheldrake**
PET LIKES: **Sleeping a lot and licking plastic carrier bags (Tesco ones to be exact)**
PET HATES: **The dog, being alone and anyone else getting the attention**
HUMAN TRAITS: **Often sits up like a human on the window ledge and talks a lot**

Recipe of the week

SAUSAGE AND BEAN PIE

Serves 4
Preparation time: 15 mins
Cooking time: 35-40 mins

4 tbsp olive oil
8 good-quality Toulouse sausages
150g (5oz) chorizo cooking sausage, sliced
2 x 400g tinned tomatoes
1 x 400g tin of cannellini beans
1 bunch of fresh flat-leaf parsley, chopped
140g (4½oz) ciabatta bread
Zest of 1 lemon, grated or peeled with a zester

1 Preheat the oven to 200°C/400°F/Gas Mark 6.

2 Heat 2 tbsp of oil in your casserole pan over a medium-high heat. Add the sausages and brown them all over, then add the chorizo and fry for a min or two. Add the beans, half the parsley and the tomatoes.

3 Pulse the torn ciabatta in a food processor until it forms rough breadcrumbs. Stir in the remaining oil, parsley, half the lemon zest and a little salt.

4 Pile the crumb mixture on top of the sausage mixture, spread out and bake in the oven for 35-40 mins or until the crust is golden and the sausages are cooked. Cover with foil if it starts to brown too much. Once cooked, sprinkle with the remaining parsley and lemon zest and serve.

Credit: The Higgidy Cookbook by Camilla Stephens. Published by Quercus £16.99
www.higgidy.co.uk

30 MONDAY

31 TUESDAY

1 WEDNESDAY

2 THURSDAY

3 FRIDAY

4 SATURDAY

5 SUNDAY

Blooming awkward!

Our wedding day was to be on February 27, 1965. We had had problems with my husband-to-be's suit, so to make sure nothing else could go wrong I got in touch with florists, photographers, caterers, etc the day before, confident everything would be fine. I had decided that my two small bridesmaids would have snowdrops attached to their muffs and my other bridesmaid carried a Bible which would have flowers to go through the pages. There were also freesias for the mums, orchids for me and carnations for the men.

My bridesmaid Margaret and I went to the hairdressers at 7.30am and came home expecting the flowers to be there. No. In a panic I went to the nearest phonebox (no home landlines then) to ring the florist – about 10 miles away. They said the flowers would arrive. Needless to say, my mom, dad and bridesmaid went to the church with no flowers.

My sister-in-law had got married the week before us. Some of her flowers had been kept in water so the groom, best man and future father-in-law used these and I got a couple of flowers to carry up the aisle.

The vicar, who asked me to be on time as he was going to a rugby match in the afternoon, calmed us down and we went ahead with the ceremony. My flowers arrived during the service and instead of being able to listen to the choir boys sing the anthem we had chosen, everyone was putting flowers on, with the vicar helping.
Mrs M Long, West Midlands

Top tip

On a cold winter's day, there's nothing like settling down with a cuppa and a classic film. But rather than forking out for a brand new DVD you'll watch once from the high street, go browse through your local library's DVD collection. Most libraries have a wide range of films, many of them old favourites that it's lovely to spend a nostalgic afternoon watching again.

Brain teaser

Here's one to drive you up the wall! Enter the solutions to the clues in their numbered layers of the wall. Each word must be an anagram of its neighbours, plus or minus one letter.

1 Sly, secretive
2 Goodness
3 Metal fastener
4 Layer
5 Wrath
6 Annoy
7 Metric unit of liquid volume
8 Rubbish dropped on the street
9 Easily snapped or broke

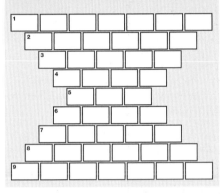

My perfect pet

NAME: **Gavin**
AGE: **5**
OWNER: **Rachel Jones**
PET LIKES: **Head-butting those he loves most and fighting with his sister, Stacey**
PET HATES: **The hoover**
HUMAN TRAITS: **Likes watching TV, especially The Hunt by Sir David Attenborough, although he has been known to try to get in the telly to join in**

Recipe of the week

CHOCOLATE GINGER BISCUITS

Makes: 18
Preparation time: 10 mins
Cooking time: 12-15 mins

150g (5oz) porridge oats
100g (3½oz) buckwheat flour
1 tbsp baking powder
1 tsp cinnamon
50g (2oz) toasted blanched hazelnuts, chopped
200g (7oz) butter
120g (4oz) tahini/smooth peanut butter
90ml (3floz) coconut oil
60ml (2floz) ginger syrup, from stem ginger
60ml (2floz) maple syrup
90g (3oz) stem ginger, finely chopped
100g (3½oz) dark chocolate, finely chopped

1 Preheat the oven to 180°C/350°F/Gas Mark 4 and line a baking tray. Combine the oats, flour, baking powder, cinnamon and chopped hazelnuts together.

2 In a saucepan, mix together the butter, tahini, coconut oil, ginger syrup and maple syrup and gently melt over a low heat until combined. Add the wet ingredients to the dry and stir, folding in the stem ginger. Roll into 18 small balls and place on the baking tray.

3 Gently flatten each ball with a fork and bake in the oven for 12-15 mins. Once cooked, allow to cool for 15 mins on the baking tray before transferring to a cooling rack.

4 While the cookies are cooling, melt the chocolate. Drizzle the chocolate over them using a teaspoon. Allow the chocolate to cool and set before eating.
Credit: Flahavan oats

6 MONDAY
_____

7 TUESDAY
_____

8 WEDNESDAY
_____

9 THURSDAY
_____

10 FRIDAY
_____

11 SATURDAY
_____

12 SUNDAY
_____

My lucky escape

My first child - a daughter - was born in hospital in 1949 and as I had had an easy birth with her I was recommended to have my next baby delivered at home. As a precaution, a doctor would be in attendance towards the end of delivery.

My midwife was very sweet but a little deaf. She had also, more seriously for me as it turned out, lost her sense of smell. By the time the doctor arrived I was about to give birth. He said to me: "You don't need a doctor, you need a fireman!" When I asked why, he informed us that he had found the electric kettle that the midwife had put on for hot water for a cup of tea must have had an element touching the stove. The wire connecting it to the plug was not to be seen, it had completely burnt away.

Obviously the midwife hadn't smelled anything. When the doctor asked me if I hadn't noticed the smell of burning, my answer was no - I had had other things on my mind! I was so lucky the house did not catch fire. My 18-month-old daughter, in the meantime, had slept right through the whole drama. My son arrived without further incident and the water for my welcome cup of tea was boiled in a saucepan. I have never stopped thinking how very lucky we all were that night.

Margaret Frankland, Sanderstead, Surrey

Top tip

To hear about exclusive offers at your favourite retailer, sign up to their email newsletter. There's usually a button somewhere on their website or there may be a form to fill in in-store. Some retailers send special discounts to their mailing list or a welcome offer for your first shop. If you later get fed up with the emails or have made the most of the introductory offers, the retailer legally has to offer you a way to unsubscribe.

Animal magic

We all had a favourite doll when we were little, and chimpanzees are no different. Babies have been observed in the wild playing make believe with sticks, pretending to feed them and cradle them.

Brain teaser

Write the pairs of letters into the circles so that each diagonal line running through the grid's centre produces a six-letter word. The key is to place the correct pair of letters in the central circle, so that they are common to all six words.

AL
BR
CH
CL
EN
ER
GL
HY
MO
NE
SM
TY
UT

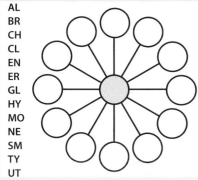

My perfect pet

NAME: **Penny**
AGE: **4 months**
OWNER: **Ann Warrior**
PET LIKES: **Having her ears rubbed**
PET HATES: **Sudden noises**
HUMAN TRAITS: **Always curious**

Recipe of the week

GARLIC CRUST CASSEROLE

Serves: 4
Preparation time: 25 mins
Cooking time: 30 mins

For the tomato sauce:
8 medium tomatoes
Small bunch of fresh basil
2 cloves garlic
1 small onion
For the casserole:
1 tbsp oil
1 medium courgette, halved
1 medium aubergine, halved
1 yellow pepper, halved
6 medium mushrooms
400g (14oz) cannellini beans
3 tbsp black olives, sliced
5cm (2in) chunks of bread
For the garlic butter:
2 tbsp butter
2 cloves garlic, minced
Small bunch of fresh basil

1 Blend the ingredients for the tomato sauce until smooth. Transfer the mix to a frying pan and bring to a simmer. Cook for 10 mins until thick. Season to taste.

2 Add the vegetables to a blender and blitz until chunky.

3 Cook the chopped vegetables for 5-10 mins, until soft. Add the cannellini beans and olives along with the tomato sauce. Mix to combine.

4 Blitz the bread into breadcrumbs. Put the butter, garlic and basil in a small bowl and melt in the microwave. Mix well.

5 Heat the oven to 190°C/375°F/Gas Mark 5. Transfer the vegetable mixture to a baking dish and top with bread. Drizzle with the garlic butter. Bake for 30 mins, until the crust is crispy and golden.

Credit: uk.russellhobbs.com/recipes

13 MONDAY

14 TUESDAY

15 WEDNESDAY

16 THURSDAY

17 FRIDAY

18 SATURDAY

19 SUNDAY

My lucky escape

This photograph brings back so many memories from my early working life. It was taken in the type-room of ICI, Nylon Works (Ardeer), Stevenston, Ayrshire, probably about 1970. The plant was in existence from 1968 to 1980 and I am the one sitting at the window, at the middle desk, beside the girl reading the document, I would have been around 28 years of age then. We were probably checking each other's work. The typewriters were still manual then and made by Adler. They were super machines, hardwearing and reliable with a lovely smooth action. When they were replaced with electric ones I was allowed to purchase my old typewriter.

To this day I have it stored away in our attic. It is like the relationship you have with a car, when you are working with a typewriter everyday you develop a very personal attachment.

It was technical work - our plant produced Nylon 6:6 Salt - there was also an ICI division nearby which produced explosives. There wasn't a supervisor as such and documents to be typed were delivered to the office and put in a box. Urgent documents were marked 'Priority'. The work was varied and came from all parts of the plant. Even worse than the technical terms was trying to read some of the writing of the authors! After some years we became knowledgeable about the jargon, which made it easier. We were never left with nothing to type!

Diana Pirrie, Kilwinning, Ayrshire

Animal magic

Flamingos get their distinctive pink hue from eating shrimp, which have carotenoids with pink pigments. If their diets were different they'd be grey.

Brain teaser

Each number in the grid indicates the number of trees in its adjacent squares. No tree can be horizontally, vertically or diagonally adjacent to another and no tree can appear in the same square as a number. Can you work out where all the trees are planted? We've placed one to help you get going.

1		1			2	
	2	1		1		
			1	2	1	
2	2	1				
		2	3		2	
	1			🌲	2	
	2					
2			1	2	1	
	2	3				
				2		

My perfect pet

NAME: **Frodo**
AGE: **2**
OWNER: **Heather Biddle**
PET LIKES: **Going to the beach with his big brother Bobby**
PET HATES: **None**
HUMAN TRAITS: **He loves watching television and putting his paws around your neck for cuddles**

Recipe of the week

LEMON SCONES

Makes: 24
Preparation time: 30 mins
Cooking time: 10-13 mins

90g (3¼oz) sultanas
225g (8oz) plain flour
2 tsp baking powder
1 large lemon, finely-grated peel
Small pinch of salt
75g (3oz) unsalted butter, softened
35g (1¼oz) caster sugar
1 medium egg, beaten
75ml (2floz) whole milk
120g (4oz) lemon curd
225g (8oz) clotted cream

1 Preheat your oven to 200°C/400°F/Gas Mark 6 then lightly grease a large baking sheet.

2 Mix the flour, baking powder, lemon peel and salt in a bowl then rub in the butter with your fingertips.

3 Stir in the sultanas, sugar, egg and milk to form a soft dough, handling as little as possible to keep it light.

4 Roll the dough until 1.5cm (½in) thick then fold half over the top of itself (this gives a nice natural break to cut them open once cooked), then flatten slightly using the palm of your hand.

5 Cut out 24 mini scones with a 4cm (1½in) cutter, re-rolling the dough as required.

6 Bake in the centre of the oven for 10-13 mins until risen and golden, then transfer to a wire rack to cool completely.

7 Once cooled split and fill the scones with lemon curd and clotted cream - delicious - enjoy!
Credit: www.whitworths.co.uk/recipies

20 MONDAY

21 TUESDAY

22 WEDNESDAY

23 THURSDAY

24 FRIDAY

25 SATURDAY

26 SUNDAY

My unlucky dip

When I was seven our class had a lovely teacher. She made up two bran tubs - one for the boys and one for the girls. She called us out two at a time and we dipped into the tubs for a prettily-wrapped gift. I was delighted with my present, a notebook and pencil. I loved to write and was always scribbling stories on the backs of old envelopes using blunt stubs of pencil so these were a real luxury to me.

I was already planning how I would use my very best handwriting on these pristine pages when the boy sitting next to me, Donald, put his hand up and reported that he had drawn out a bottle of scent. Our teacher was immediately contrite. A girl's present had got into the boys' bran tub. She asked me to swap with Donald.

I clutched my precious notebook closer to me and looked miserable, but the teacher said: "Go behind the blackboard and come to an agreement, you two."

So I had to hand over my lovely notebook and pencil and went home thoroughly disgruntled. A bottle of 'stinky scent'! That was what we called the cheap-shop perfume. Evening in Paris was the only one we found acceptable and regarded as the height of luxury.

Now that I'm in my 80s I still love notebooks and always have several of them on the go at once. Perhaps, I am still trying to make up for that early bitter disappointment.
Mrs D Parry, Southport

Top tip

A nifty way to save a little money on your home insurance is to join your local Neighbourhood Watch as some home insurers offer a nice discount for Neighbourhood Watch Scheme members. To find your nearest scheme, contact your local neighbourhood policing team or visit www.ourwatch.org.uk. If there isn't one in your area, you can set one up. You'll also usually get a lower home insurance quote if you install an alarm and extra locks.

Brain teaser

Shade in one letter in each box of this grid to form a crossword. Proper nouns are not allowed.

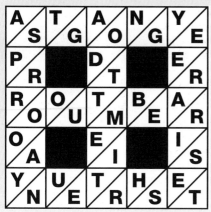

A/S	T/G	A/O	N/G	Y/E
P/R	■	D/T	■	E/R
R/O	T/U	B/M	E/E	A/R
O/A	■	E/I	■	I/S
Y/N	U/E	T/R	H/S	E/T

My perfect pet

NAME: **Marmite**

AGE: **9**

OWNER: **Sallyann Bowman**

PET LIKES: **Hiding in shopping bags and jumping out at unsuspecting passers by and playing with 'stringy' things**

PET HATES: **The cat from next door coming into her garden**

HUMAN TRAITS: **If Marmite is up in the morning, everyone has to be up. If meowing doesn't wake people, she'll jump on the bed**

Recipe of the week

PESTO AND WATERCRESS SOUP

Serves: 3
Preparation time: 10 mins
Cooking time: 5 mins

1 tbsp oil
1 onion, sliced
3 cloves of garlic, minced
1 avocado
250g (9oz) mixed green leaves (spinach, watercress and rocket)
4g flaked almonds (plus extra 1 tbsp of flaked almonds), toasted
1 tbsp basil pesto
500ml (18floz) hot vegetable stock
2 tbsp Greek yogurt, to serve
Salt
Pepper

1 Heat the oil in a frying pan, and add the onion and garlic and cook for 5 mins over a medium heat, until the onion and garlic are soft and fragrant.

2 Transfer the cooked vegetables to blender, along with the avocado, leaves, pesto, almonds and the vegetable stock. Add everything except the extra tbsp of almonds and the Greek yogurt. If all of the salad leaves don't fit, add the leaves a handful at a time to make the processer easier.

3 Blitz everything until the soup mixture is completely smooth, the time this takes will depend on the efficiency of your blender. Season to taste, then serve, topped with the Greek yogurt and a few more flaked almonds that have been toasted in a frying pan for 5 mins, until golden and brown.

Credit: uk.russellhobbs.com

27 MONDAY

28 TUESDAY

1 WEDNESDAY

2 THURSDAY

3 FRIDAY

4 SATURDAY

5 SUNDAY

Five-finger typing

This photograph is of my first job after leaving school in 1957 – I'm standing at the back in the middle between Jean and Pam. We all worked for Evered at Smethwick. We are all still friends today and meet up when we can - even though one girl now lives in Australia. She comes back every four years and we still talk about our times together and the fun we had.

The photograph was taken to celebrate the arrival of our new typewriters. The ones we had used before were the old tin bone-shakers, as we called them. I was the junior and still learning to type. I must admit that at first I did rather well with just two fingers, but then went to night school. In the beginning, I found it very hard using all my fingers and not looking at the keys! Viera (she is the one sitting at the typewriter), wouldn't hesitate to rap me across the fingers with a ruler when she saw me using two fingers and that finally did the trick.

I am now retired, but graduated from a manual typewriter, to an electric and then to a computer by the time I left. It was wonderful not having to line multiple copies up and use Tippex! Everything was so much quicker and easier to correct if you made a mistake. But while it is certainly different today in the office, I'm not sure that they have as much fun as we did.

Pat Justin, Smethwick, W Mids

Top tip

Every March and October is Free Wills Month, which is a great opportunity to get your last wishes drafted out for free by a solicitor. That's a saving of upwards of £100. You must be over 55 and you'll need to search freewillsmonth.org.uk to find the solicitors near you who are taking part. As the scheme is backed by charities, you may be asked to consider making a charitable bequest in your will, but you're under no obligation.

Animal magic

They may be tiny, furry and mouse-like in appearance, but amazingly it turns out that the elephant shrew's closest relative is the elephant, rather than the shrew.

Brain teaser

Fill the blank squares in this grid with digits so that each row, each column and each of the 3 x 3 blocks contains all the digits 1 to 9 once and once only.

		2						6
	6			7			1	
4	5	2	6		1			7
			9			3		
9	4						5	1
		6			2			
6			1		5	7	9	3
	9			8			2	
5					6			

My perfect pet

NAME: **Ella**
AGE: **3 months when this photo was taken**
OWNER: **The Scotts**
PET LIKES: **Cuddles and more cuddles**
PET HATES: **The hairdryer**
HUMAN TRAITS: **Thinks she can answer the doorbell and the phone**

Recipe of the week

BLUEBERRY PANCAKES

Serves: 4-6
Preparation time: 5 mins
Cooking time: 15 mins

225g (8oz) plain flour
1 tbsp golden caster sugar
Pinch of salt
2 large eggs, beaten
1 tbsp of vanilla extract
110g (4oz) low-fat vanilla yogurt
200ml (6¾floz) organic milk
150g (5oz) blueberries
150ml (5floz) maple syrup
3-4 tbsp vegetable or rapeseed oil

1 Add the plain flour, caster sugar and salt to a mixing bowl and mix together with a wooden spoon. Make a well in the middle and whisk in the eggs, vanilla, yogurt and milk. Combine with a whisk into a thick batter. Heat a tbsp of the oil in a frying pan.

2 Spoon roughly 3 tbsp of the batter into the hot pan. The mixture will be frothing and sizzling. When it starts to create little air bubbles pop three or four blueberries into the pancake and then flip over with a spatula.

3 Cook until golden brown. Stack around three or four on top of each other.

4 Once you have cooked the desired amount of pancakes in the hot pan put 6 tbsp of maple syrup and quickly add around 10 blueberries.
Credit: Rachel's Organic Yogurt

6 MONDAY

7 TUESDAY

8 WEDNESDAY

9 THURSDAY

10 FRIDAY

11 SATURDAY

12 SUNDAY

Third time lucky

I finally passed my driving test at the third attempt in 1977, at the age of 45 - around the same time as this photo was taken. My lady instructor was also teaching my son to drive. "If only," she said longingly after one lesson, "you had your son's confidence and he had your smoothness of drive, I would be a happy woman." I failed miserably the first time I took my test because I had a fire engine chasing up behind me with sirens blaring. As you can imagine, it shot my nerves to pieces. And after that it was downhill all the way.

Finally, in spite of many warnings, my husband took over teaching me and we had several arguments. On one occasion I stopped the car, got out and sat in the back saying: "Okay, clever clogs, you do it!"Or words to that effect. However, he wasn't prepared to do that and said: "Get back behind that wheel, or sit there all night."

After a while I did pass, two weeks before my first grandson was born - on the seventh of the seventh, seventy-seven. This meant I was able to drive proudly over to help my daughter with the baby. But I was never a confident driver and now, at 84, I am content to let everyone else drive me. My husband, bless him, is no longer with us, but we used to have many a laugh about the driving lessons he gave me.

Jean Johnson, Kent

Top tip

If you wear glasses, you could save yourself a fortune just by looking in the right places. First, see if any high street opticians are offering free eye tests. Then after your check-up, make use of your legal right to request a copy of your prescription and compare the cost of specs from place to place until you find the cheapest. Online discount suppliers often have glasses for a fraction of the cost you pay on the high street.

Animal magic

Before they hatch, chicks talk to each other from inside their eggs. Scientists have recorded at least 24 different sounds from these chatty fluff-balls.

Brain teaser

Enter single-digit numbers into the empty triangles in this grid so that the figures in each hexagon add up to 26. No two numbers can appear twice in the same hexagon and nought cannot be used.

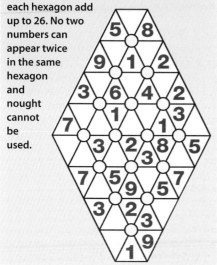

My perfect pet

NAME: **Jasper**
AGE: **3**
OWNER: **Helen Kavanagh**
PET LIKES: **Cat treats, his cat friends and cuddles**
PET HATES: **The coat hood and sudden noises**
HUMAN TRAITS: **Tries to get human food and taps humans for attention**

Recipe of the week

SALMON AND BUTTER BEAN MASH

Serves: 2
Preparation time: 1-2 hrs
Cooking time: 8-10 mins

2 x 125g (4oz) salmon fillets
1 tbsp olive oil
1 tbsp balsamic vinegar
Juice of half lemon
Handful of chopped parsley
For the dill sauce:
100ml (3½oz) plain yogurt/Alpro soya
2 tbsp low-fat mayonnaise
5cm (2in) cucumber, finely chopped
4 tbsp fresh dill, chopped
Salt and pepper, to taste
For the mash:
420g (15oz) can butter beans, drained and rinsed
6 tbsp milk/Alpro soya
4 spring onions, finely chopped

1 Preheat the oven to 190°C/375°F/Gas Mark 5. Combine all ingredients for the dill sauce in a food processor and blend. Pour into bowl and refrigerate for 1-2 hrs. Mix 1 tbsp oil, balsamic, lemon juice and parsley. Place the salmon, skin side up, in an oven proof dish, season and pour over the marinade. Rest for 10 mins. Cook the salmon for 8-10 mins.

2 Place the butter beans and 150ml (¼pt) cold water in a pan. Simmer for 5 mins. Mash with a potato masher. Return to the pan; add the milk and spring onions and mix.

3 Serve the salmon on a bed of butterbean mash with a spoonful of sauce.
Credit: Alpro

13 MONDAY

14 TUESDAY

15 WEDNESDAY

16 THURSDAY

17 FRIDAY

18 SATURDAY

19 SUNDAY

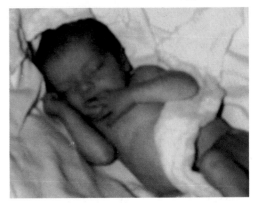

Just the two of us

Thirty years ago, after the miners' strike had just ended, my husband was spending Mothering Sunday with his late mother. My elder sister and her daughter were visiting our mother just a few streets away. At that time, only a few houses had landline telephones - and we weren't one of them. I was 39 and my baby was due in the following weeks. I was alone in the house and my neighbours were all visiting their mothers. It was a lovely day - March 17.

I suddenly felt as though there was a lot of movement, then some pain. I happened to be in the kitchen and could not move at all. I realised things were going very fast. So I pulled out some clean tablecloths and towels, grabbed the scissors to cut the cord, then kneeling on the towels and tablecloths, I waited for the inevitable. After about an hour there was a final strong contraction and there on the pile of towels lay my lovely new baby boy. I was so thrilled.

He opened his eyes and looked at me - they were sky-blue just like his dad's. I tied the cord tightly in two places, four inches apart and cut the umbilical cord. As my baby was very clean, I just wrapped him in towels and cuddled him. I felt fine, so I stood up, walked around the house, found my camera and took photos. After 20 minutes, just the two of us together, I let the world and my family know about him. I did not wish to go to hospital, I stayed home and enjoyed my baby.

Meryl Dixon, Aberdare, S Wales

Animal magic

Dolphins have names. They use a unique click or whistle to identify one another, and always respond when they hear their own name call.

Brain teaser

See if you can work out the answer to this problem:

A driver refuses to let a man onto his bus, saying: "It is forbidden to bring any object with a length, width, or depth greater than one metre on any bus. That vegetable you're carrying is longer than one metre." "You're right," grins the man. "This cucumber is 1.2 metres long and it should win me first prize at the village fair. I can buy another ticket for it if you like." "No," replies the driver, "rules are rules. You cannot get on the bus with it." The man dashes into a nearby shop and comes out with a package containing the cucumber. He shows it to the driver who pulls out a folding rule and measures it. Scowling, he waves on the smug man. How did the man manage this feat without chopping up his record-breaking veg?

My perfect pet

NAME: **Max**
AGE: **9**
OWNER: **Deborah Townsend**
PET LIKES: **Begging for food and his squeaky toys**
PET HATES: **Thunder, heavy rain and fireworks**
HUMAN TRAITS: **If he needs anything he waves his paw at you. That's his way of asking**

Recipe of the week

BANOFFEE MUFFINS

Makes: 12
Preparation time: 20 mins
Cooking time: 40 mins

225g (8oz) wholewheat plain flour
1 tsp bicarbonate of soda
115g (4oz) light brown sugar
50g (2oz) walnuts, finely chopped
Medium egg beaten
200ml (6¾floz) buttermilk
4 tbsp of oil
1 large ripe banana, peeled and mashed
2 tsp of caramel flavour/extract
12 dried banana chips

1 Preheat the oven to 190°C/375°F/Gas Mark 5. Line a muffin tin with 12 muffin cases. Sift the flour and bicarbonate of soda into a mixing bowl, adding any husks that remain behind in the sieve. Stir in the sugar and walnuts. Make a well in the centre of the mixture for when you add in the liquids.

2 In a measuring jug, mix together the egg, buttermilk, oil, mashed banana and caramel flavour. Pour into the well and mix to form a thick batter.

3 Spoon the batter into the muffin cases, making sure you place an even amount in each. Put a banana chip on top of each and bake in the oven for about 20 mins, until risen and lightly golden. Transfer the muffins to a wire rack to cool. Serve warm or cold.
Credit: Whitworths

20 MONDAY

21 TUESDAY

22 WEDNESDAY

23 THURSDAY

24 FRIDAY

25 SATURDAY

26 SUNDAY

Hair today...

When I was born in the Forties, they discovered I had a club foot. The nearest hospital where I had to go for operations was in Oxford - the Wingfield Hospital as it was known then. This meant that my mum had to travel to see me by public transport all the way from Earley (near Reading) to visit me. Not a mean feat by any means. This story was related to me many times...

When she arrived one day she couldn't see me anywhere and asked the nurse where I was. When they pointed me out, she found out why. My ringlets had gone - they had simply cut them off! It would not be allowed today! Fresh air was also considered the best treatment for us and so we were all pushed outside in our beds through big glass doors that opened up during the day. There was no hospital transport then.

Mum also had to travel with me to and from Oxford by public transport to get my plaster cast changed. I often wonder how many changes of bus she had to make all together. I never heard her complain though.

The good thing is that they did a really good job on my foot which is now 70 years old and still doing everything I ask from it. Buying shoes is, frankly, a nightmare as I have such different sized feet, but at least I have two feet.

Di Vaughan, Didcot, Oxon

Top tip

Planning a summer holiday or day trips out with the grandchildren? Book your train tickets 12 weeks in advance to get the best price. Network Rail have to set their timetable 12 weeks ahead and the cheapest advance tickets usually come out shortly after this. If you're online, you can sign up The Trainline's ticket alert system on www. thetrainline.com/ticketalert so you'll get an email when the cheapest advance tickets for the specific journey you want to make come on sale.

Animal magic

Polar bears have black skin under their thick white fur. It helps them to keep cosy, as black is better at absorbing the sun's rays.

Brain teaser

The symbols in this grid all represent a number between one and nine. When a symbol appears twice in a square it is doubled. The figure at the end of each row and column is the sum of the numbers in it. Can you work out which number each symbol represents?

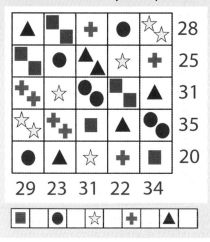

My perfect pet

NAME: **Poppy**
AGE: **2**
OWNER: **Julie Moffat**
PET LIKES: **Howling in the morning to get me out of bed**
PET HATES: **Going to bed at night**
HUMAN TRAITS: **Eating cheese as a treat**

Recipe of the week

LEMON TART

Serves: 4-6
Preparation time: 40 mins
Cooking time: 30 mins

Pre-made shortcrust pastry tart case
4 medium eggs
100g (3½oz) caster sugar
80ml (2¾oz) freshly squeezed lemon juice
2 tbsp lemon zest
120ml (4oz) cream or an alternative to cream
Icing sugar for dusting

1 Preheat your oven to 140°C/275°F/Gas Mark 1. Whisk together the eggs, caster sugar, lemon juice and zest until the mixture is light and frothy. Slowly add in the cream, whisking as you go.

2 Pour the mixture into a medium-sized pan and gently warm through, while keeping on a low heat. Be careful not to heat the mixture too much as you will end up with scrambled eggs, this process is just to speed up the cooking of the tart and help the mixture set nicely. If you think the mixture is curdling then take it off the heat immediately and sieve out any lumps.

3 Place the pastry case on a baking tray and pour in the warmed lemon mixture. Place in the preheated oven for 25 mins until just set. Remove from the oven and leave to cool for a least 1 hr. Dust with icing sugar before serving.
Credit: Alpro

27 MONDAY

28 TUESDAY

29 WEDNESDAY

30 THURSDAY

31 FRIDAY

1 SATURDAY

2 SUNDAY

Spot the typing mistake!

That's me in the typing pool, the last girl on the left at the back of the picture, sitting under the poster on the wall. The year is 1973, I was 17 and had followed in my sister's footsteps by becoming a trainee typist with the Automobile Association (AA). The centralised typing centre was on the eleventh floor of Farnum House, the organisation's headquarters in Basingstoke.

I had learned to type on a manual typewriter and it was very strange – and a bit frightening – when I had to learn to control an electric typewriter. The one I used back then was an Adler.

This photo makes me smile because it was taken to promote the audio equipment we were using at the time. As any good audio typist will know, you couldn't cross your legs when you were audio typing because you had to control the machine with a foot pedal. If you look closely you will spot that Norma, sitting in the front wearing a checked pinafore dress, has her legs crossed under the desk!

After attending evening classes for two years to learn shorthand I moved to the Overseas Motoring department and eventually became PA to the Public Relations Manager. I eventually left the AA in 1989 but am still in touch with two of the friends, Maria Blackman and Pauline Owen, I made when we were all girls together in the typing pool 40 years ago.
Chris Horton, Hook

Top tip

Had a spring clean of your wardrobe and wondering what to do with all your old clothes you don't want? Host a swishing party where you invite friends and neighbours to bring along their unwanted clothing and you all swap. One woman's rubbish is often another's treasure and you never know what gems you might be able to get your hands on – for free!

Brain teaser

All of the vowels have been removed from this completed crossword. Simply put them back where they belong, using only the vowels from the lists below. Remember to cross out each vowel as you place it in the grid, or you may well end up in a vowel mess!

A A A A A A A A   E E E E E E E E
I I I I I I I I   O O O O O O O U U U

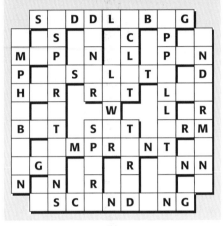

My perfect pet

NAMES: **Charlie and Pandora**
AGE: **Charlie, 4, Pandora, 2**
OWNER: **Anne Bartlett**
PET LIKES: **Parsley, popcorn, tunnels, cuddles and each other**
PET HATES: **Being without each other, having a bath and having their nails clipped**
HUMAN TRAITS: **Talking to you, well, squeaking, when you're in the same room as them**

Recipe of the week

SPAGHETTI AND TUNA BALLS

Makes: 20
Preparation time: 25 mins
Cooking time: 10 mins

2 x 200g (7oz) tinned tuna drained
½ tsp chilli flakes
2 garlic cloves, peeled and finely chopped
50g (2oz) pine nuts, toasted
Zest of 1 lemon
80g (3oz) fresh breadcrumbs
20g (1oz) parsley, roughly chopped
1 large free-range egg, beaten
375g (13oz) spaghetti
3 tbsp Filippo Berio Olive Oil
300g Passata or tomato sauce
Extra virgin olive oil for drizzling

1 Flake the tuna into a large bowl and mix in the chilli flakes, garlic, pine nuts, lemon zest, parsley, breadcrumbs and egg. Season with salt and fresh black pepper.

2 Wet your hands and roll the tuna mixture into walnut-sized balls. Place on to a large tray and chill for 10 mins. Meanwhile, heat up a large pan of boiling water and cook the pasta according to packet instructions.

3 Heat the olive oil in a large frying pan. Cook the tuna balls for 5-7 mins, turning occasionally until golden. Heat up the tomato sauce and add to the pasta. Top with the tuna balls. Serve immediately with a drizzle of extra virgin olive oil.
Credit: www.filippoberio.co.uk

3 MONDAY

4 TUESDAY

5 WEDNESDAY

6 THURSDAY

7 FRIDAY

8 SATURDAY

9 SUNDAY

There was jiving in Brighton

Back in the Fifties Lonnie Donegan took skiffle music into the hit parade with numbers such as Rock Island Line and Cumberland Gap. In Liverpool, it inspired John Lennon to form The Quarrymen and similar groups sprang up all over the country. For ten months I was part of one such group called The Chessmen.

There were three lads with guitars, one lad on bass (this was made of a wooden tea chest, a broom handle and string) and myself on the metal washboard, complete with thimbles on my fingers.

We played in pubs, clubs, holiday camps and at parties, weddings and dances. The leader of the group would sing at the drop of a hat. If we were having a cup of tea in a café he would ask if we could perform for the other customers.

One Sunday in April 1958 we all squashed into someone's Mini Minor (plus our instruments) and drove to Brighton where we played on the seafront. We attracted quite a crowd and soon there were youngsters jiving to our music. I still have this photo taken by one of the guitarists – I'm wearing a jacket as it was quite a chilly day.

We made several demo tapes that we sent off to various record companies but fame and fortune passed us by. Nevertheless, I had a terrific time with The Chessmen and still have lots of wonderful, funny memories.

Pat Rose, Sidmouth

Top tip

Make the most of those April showers by collecting rainwater to use on your garden come summer. All you need is a basic plastic water butt you can pick up from most DIY stores - some local councils even offer reduced priced water butts to residents. Go for a model that has a tap at the base to make things easier. Remember rain water is free and could save you plenty on your water bill later.

Animal magic

If you ever sucked your thumb as a baby, you're in good company. Baby elephants have been known to suck their trunks to comfort themselves too - so sweet!

Brain teaser

Fill the blank squares in this grid with digits so that each row, each column and each of the 3 x 3 blocks contains all the digits 1 to 9 once and once only.

2			4		6			3
				5				
5		3				6		8
		1	8	3	9	2		
		7				5		
		4	7	2	5	8		
9		8				7		4
				4				
4			6		3			1

My perfect pet

NAME: **Ned**
AGE: **9 weeks old**
OWNER: **Kelly Owen**
PET LIKES: **Milk, on everything. Especially stealing it from others**
PET HATES: **Not being able to be nosey**
HUMAN TRAITS: **Demands to be cuddled regularly**

Recipe of the week

SIMNEL APRICOT AND PECAN CAKE

Serves: 10
Preparation time: 20 mins
Cooking time: 60 mins

175g (6oz) butter, softened
175g (6oz) light soft brown sugar
3 large British Lion eggs, beaten
225g (8oz) self-raising flour, sieved
1 tsp baking powder
100g (3½oz) sultanas
225g (8oz) no-soak apricots, chopped
Zest and juice of 1 orange
100g (3½oz) pecan nuts, chopped
To decorate:
500g pack of marzipan
100g (3½oz) chocolate, melted

1 Preheat the oven 170°C/325°F/Gas Mark 3. Grease a 20cm (8in) round, deep cake tin and line.

2 Place the butter, sugar, eggs, flour and baking powder in a large bowl. Whisk until smooth and glossy. Fold in the remaining ingredients and spoon into the tin. Bake for 1-1½hrs until risen and firm.

3 Use a sharp knife to split the cake in half through the middle. Roll out two thirds of the marzipan on an icing sugar-dusted surface and cut out two 20cm (8in) rounds. Brush both cut surfaces of the cake with jam and sandwich together with one of the marzipan rounds.

4 Brush the top with jam and arrange the second marzipan round on top, crimp the edges. Roll the remaining marzipan into 11 balls and arrange on top, attaching with jam.

5 Spoon the chocolate into a piping bag and drizzle over the top.
Credit: British Lion Eggs

10 MONDAY

11 TUESDAY

12 WEDNESDAY

13 THURSDAY

14 FRIDAY

15 SATURDAY

16 SUNDAY

A testing time

This photo, taken in the Fifties, is of me putting the L plates on our Ford Prefect. When the time came for me to take my driving test, my father drove me to the test centre in Kendal. I went into the office and was told to wait by my vehicle. When the tester came out his first comment was: "Why have you parked here? It's no waiting on this side today." Luckily, my dad took the blame. Next he asked to see my provisional driving licence and demanded: "Do you know you have been driving illegally for six weeks as you haven't signed this?" I duly signed.

Halfway through my three-point turn, the tester asked: "Who taught you to drive?" When I told him it was my mum, he said: "She has done a good job." I began to feel better. After doing a reverse turn, we proceeded up the main street. Without asking me to do an emergency stop or a hill start, he announced that I was "...all right and could take him home for dinner."

Somewhat surprised by this, I queried whether there would be any questions on The Highway Code. He replied: "All right. What's the sign for a school?" When I promptly replied 'a flaming torch' he laughed and said: "No need to get aerated about it!" He then handed me a pink slip which I had to take to the County Hall to get my licence stamped. A first-time pass - it made my day!
Bryan Park, Whitley Bay

Top tip

It's a real shame to throw spoiled food away and not to mention a waste of money. To try and avoid too much going off, store your milk, bread, eggs, cheese and even nuts in the freezer. That way you can eat them at your own pace and won't have to throw so much in the bin. You can even freeze chopped up fresh herbs - just press them in ice cube trays and cover with a tiny bit of water then stick them in the fridge. Then when you're ready to eat them, pop the cubes into a freezer bag to thaw.

Brain teaser

Each number in the grid indicates the number of trees in its adjacent squares. No tree can be horizontally, vertically or diagonally adjacent to another and no tree can appear in the same square as a number. Can you work out where all the trees are planted? We've placed one to help you get going.

	2				2		
1	1	2			2		3
		2					
1			🌳	2		2		2
1	2		2		1	1	
	2		2				
	2				3		
		3					2
				1			

My perfect pet

NAMES: **Cherrie (left) and Blossom (right)**
AGE: **3**
OWNER: **Gillian Jackson**
PET LIKES: **Singing along to Eighties music, especially the Pet Shop Boys and Duran Duran.**
PET HATES: **April showers. If they could figure out how to hold a brolly with their paws they would!**
HUMAN TRAITS: **Dancing on two legs to ABBA songs when they get excited. Dancing to Queen is their favourite!**

Recipe of the week

HOT CROSS BUNS

Serves: 12
Preparation time: 2 hrs
Cooking time: 20 mins

300ml (½pt) full-fat milk
50g (2oz) unsalted butter
500g (1¼lb) sieved strong bread flour
60g (2¼oz) caster sugar
10g (½oz) fast acting yeast
1 beaten egg
1 tsp salt
100g (3½oz) dark chocolate
1 zest of an orange
1 apple, cored and finely chopped
For the cross:
80g (2½oz) sieved plain flour
For the glaze:
20ml (1floz) milk
8 tbsp honey

1 Bring the milk to the boil then take off the heat and add the butter. Leave until warm.

2 Mix the flour, sugar, salt and yeast. Make a well in the centre and pour in your warm milk/butter and egg to create a paste - keep going until it forms a dough. Knead for 10 mins. Leave for 1 hr to prove.

3 Once risen add chocolate, apple and orange zest. Divide by 12 - each bun should weigh about 90g (3¼oz).

4 Form into neat shapes and place on to a baking tray. Lightly score a cross into each bun. Cover with oiled clingfilm and leave to rise for another hour. Once risen, glaze with milk.

5 To make the cross, mix 80g flour and 8 tbsp of water to form a paste. Pipe crosses on to the buns. Put into a preheated oven 220°C/425°F/Gas Mark 7 for 20 mins. Once your buns are baked heat the honey and glaze.
Credit: Pink Lady

17 MONDAY

18 TUESDAY

19 WEDNESDAY

20 THURSDAY

21 FRIDAY

22 SATURDAY

23 SUNDAY

Knit one, purl one...

These days I knit just to keep my hands moving – mostly mittens and scarves that end up in the charity bag – but the first item I remember knitting was a bright yellow kettle holder in the shape of a banana which we made at school. Later on, when I was 13 and a member of the Girls' Life Brigade I earned a badge by knitting a jumper. Aged 16, I started courting my future husband and I remember knitting him a sleeveless pullover in a horrible bright blue colour. (He did wear it!)

Many years later, I had set my heart on having a beautiful sweater with sheep motifs all over it like the one I'd seen Lady Diana wearing on her engagement to Prince Charles. I could do hand knitting, but certainly not well enough to make a jumper like Lady Di's.

I couldn't afford the upmarket prices for a similar one so there was nothing for it but to buy a secondhand knitting machine. Disaster! Even the vests I knitted for Ethiopian refugees were rejected and, bad news, the machine did not knit patterns. Next came a brand new machine. It was an investment, according to the salesman. And eventually (a very long eventually) I did knit myself this beautiful pink sweater decorated with navy-blue sheep. I loved it and wore it constantly. My husband said it would have been cheaper to buy the pricey upmarket sweater in the first place. Men! They just don't understand.

Mrs Pat Berkshire, Hexham

Top tip

Calling all green-fingered gardeners! Save yourself a pricey trip to the garden centre by going through your rubbish. Old tights make great soft-ties for climbing and fruit plants, while empty yogurt pots, toilet roll tubes and meat trays make great seed trays and plant pots. You can also use egg boxes for chitting potatoes, lolly sticks as plant labels and even old woolly jumpers for lining your hanging baskets.

Brain teaser

Here's one to drive you up the wall! Enter the solutions to the clues in their numbered layers of the wall. Each word must be an anagram of its neighbours, plus or minus one letter.

1 Large spotted feline
2 Door-to-door salesman
3 Appeal earnestly to
4 Distribute cards
5 Beer
6 Delicate decorative fabric
7 Transparent
8 Baby's bed
9 Announce officially

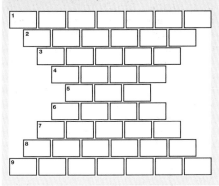

My perfect pet

NAME: **Maisie**
AGE: **16**
OWNER: **Clare and Neil Kotschy**
PET LIKES: **Laying on the sofa snoring, spitting at next door's cat through the glass and trying any food owners eat**
PET HATES: **Next door's cat, being brushed and having to move along the sofa if she's in the way**
HUMAN TRAITS: **Sulking if she's given food she doesn't fancy that day**

Recipe of the week

RAISIN TIFFIN

Makes: 9 squares
Preparation time: 10 mins
Chilling time: 1 hr

100g (3½oz) unsalted butter
25g (1oz) soft brown sugar
3 tbsp cocoa powder
4 tbsp golden syrup
10 digestive biscuits, broken into small pieces
50g (2oz) Whitworths raisins
200g (7oz) milk chocolate, broken into chunks

1 Grease and line an 18cm (7in) square brownie baking tin.

2 Mix the butter, sugar, cocoa and golden syrup together in a saucepan over a low heat for 5 mins, until the butter has melted and the sugar dissolved.

3 Remove from the heat and stir until it becomes thick and sauce like.

4 Stir in the biscuit pieces and the jumbo raisin mix until well coated in the sauce.

5 Spoon the mixture into the prepared baking tin.

6 Boil 300ml (½pt) of water in a saucepan and then remove from the heat.

7 Place the broken chocolate into a bowl and place the bowl on top of the saucepan of boiled water until melted.

8 Stir the melted chocolate and pour over top of the tiffin mix in the baking tin, use the back of a spoon to smooth the top.

9 Chill in fridge for an hour before turning out of the tin and cutting into 9 squares.
Credit: Whitworths

24 MONDAY

25 TUESDAY

26 WEDNESDAY

27 THURSDAY

28 FRIDAY

29 SATURDAY

30 SUNDAY

In quarantine

When I was eight years old, in 1946, I woke one morning to find a bright red rash all over my body. I guessed at once that I had scarlet fever, which was thought to be very infectious at that time. My brother Geoff, who was eight years older than me, had been ill with the same thing a few weeks before. When he was in the fever hospital (Rosehill, which was only 200 yards from where we lived near Rotherham) he managed to escape from the ward and sit on a swing in the large garden. I used to climb the high surrounding wall and throw him sweets.

When I became ill Dad carried me the short distance to the same hospital where I stayed for a month. I was in isolation and had a room to myself with a big window. My mum and dad were not allowed in and had to talk to me through the window. They held up a board with messages written on it. My friends at school sent me letters and drew get well pictures for me, but when I was discharged I was not allowed to bring them home as everything, including my clothes, books and toys, had to be burnt when I left.

The nurses were lovely and I was looked after very well. Considering that food was scarce so soon after the war, we were also fed well, mostly stews and vegetables with the occasional sponge pudding as a treat.

Mrs Joan Dearden, Mexborough

Top tip

When unpacking your food shop, take a little time to re-arrange your cupboards by order of use-by date. So put the stuff with the earliest dates within easy reach, while the products you've just bought that have a longer shelf-life can live at the back. This way you're less likely to end up throwing out and wasting rotten food you've forgotten about from the back of your shelves.

Animal magic

Rats and mice have a ticklish spot, and will make a squeaking 'laugh' when touched there. We feel quite jealous of the scientists whose job it is to tickle little rodents for a living.

Brain teaser

Your task is to fit the letters into the grid. Each row and column should contain one each of the letters A, B, C, D and one blank square. A letter beside a row or column indicates the first of the four letters encountered when going in the direction of the arrow.

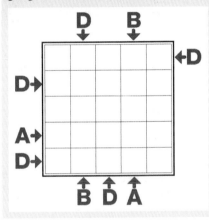

My perfect pet

NAME: **Charlie and Dudley**
AGE: **20 months and 3 years**
OWNER: **Jacqui Beckenham**
PET LIKES: **Spending time in the local woods**
PET HATES: **Having their nails clipped**
HUMAN TRAITS: **They love a cuddle in bed in the morning**

Recipe of the week

CURRIED SHOULDER OF LAMB

Serves: 8
Preparation time: 15 mins
Cooking time: 2 hrs

2.5kg (approx) shoulder Welsh lamb
1tbsp oil
1 onion, roughly chopped
2 cloves garlic, chopped
2½cm (1in) piece root ginger, peeled and chopped
30ml (2tbsp) garam masala or medium curry powder
1tsp chilli powder
400g (14oz) tinned chopped tomatoes
400g (14oz) can chickpeas
300ml (½pt) lamb stock
2 large potatoes, washed and cut into large cubes
2 large handfuls spinach

1 Preheat oven to 180ºC/350ºF/Gas Mark 4.

2 Heat a large roasting pan on the hob and add oil, onion, garlic and ginger. Add the shoulder of lamb and brown well.

3 Add the spices and coat meat in them well by rubbing them into the skin. Add the tomatoes, chickpeas, stock and potatoes. Bring to the boil, cover with foil and place in preheated oven. Cook for about 2 hrs until the meat falls off the bone. Add the spinach in the last 10 mins of cooking and allow to just wilt slightly.

4 Serve up the lamb in chunks with naan breads or steamed rice and plenty of chutney.

Credit: hwww.eatwelshlambandwelshbeef.com/en/

1 MONDAY

2 TUESDAY

3 WEDNESDAY

4 THURSDAY

5 FRIDAY

6 SATURDAY

7 SUNDAY

My lovely mum-in-law

This charming photo is of my late mother-in-law. Her name was Louise but she was always just Mum to me. It was taken when the company she worked for was evacuated to escape the bombing around St Paul's Cathedral in London. I believe the company belonged to the Vestey family and the tree was in the grounds of their country estate.

Having been brought up as one of six children with no TV for entertainment, Louise knew lots of card games which she told me made her popular with her male colleagues at this time as none of the other girls knew how to play Solo or Cribbage.

After the war, she married the man she met when they were both members of their local amateur dramatic society in Essex and appeared in a production of Gilbert and Sullivan. They settled in Gloucestershire where they brought up their family in a house with a beautiful view across to the Malvern Hills.

My mother-in-law modestly described herself as 'a good plain cook' but her pastry was the best I have ever tasted, especially her mince pies, oozing with homemade rum butter. She made jams and chutneys with produce from their garden as well as pickled walnuts - perfect with cold meat and bubble and squeak for Monday supper.

Louise lived well into her nineties. Sadly, her last years were overshadowed by dementia, but she retained her sweet nature to the end and never failed to greet me with that very special smile.
Mary Clarke, Norfolk

Top tip

Has your plastic kettle turned black inside? There's no need to spend money on a new kettle, you can easily clean it out. Just cut a lemon into slices and put these inside the kettle along with some fresh water. Bring the kettle to the boil and leave overnight. Then empty out the next day and your kettle should be shiny and clean.

Brain teaser

A fleet of ten ships is hidden in the grid. They might be lying horizontally or vertically, but they must not appear in adjacent squares, even diagonally. The numbers along the side and top of the grid show you how many parts of ships can be found in each row or column. In each case, three hits and a patch of empty sea have been filled in for you.

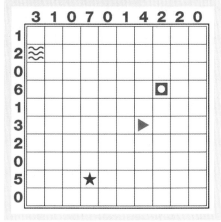

Recipe of the week

POTATO AND ASPARAGUS FLAN

Serves: 6-8
Preparation time: 30 mins
Cooking time: 50 mins

450g (1lb) Jersey Royals, scrubbed and cut into chunks
250g (9oz) asparagus
500g pack ready-to-use shortcrust pastry
3 eggs
300ml pot crème fraîche
2x100g packs Somerset goat's cheese (with rind), sliced
Salt and freshly ground black pepper
Fresh herbs, to garnish

1 Cook the Jersey Royals until just tender. Drain well, then cool. At the same time, cook the asparagus in a small amount of boiling water for 3-4 mins. Drain, then rinse with cold water to cool quickly.

2 Preheat the oven to 200°C/Gas Mark 6.

3 Roll out the pastry and line a 20x30cm (8x12in) oblong tart tin. Line with a piece of foil or greaseproof paper and baking beans and bake 'blind' for 15 mins.

4 Take the flan from the oven and remove the foil or paper and baking beans. Reduce the oven temperature to 180°C/Gas Mark 4.

5 Arrange the Jersey Royals over the base of the flan with the asparagus. Beat together the eggs and crème fraîche. Season. Pour into the flan case and arrange the sliced cheese on top. Bake for 30-35 mins, until set. Serve warm with fresh herbs.
Credit: www.jerseyroyals.co.uk

My perfect pet

NAME: **Alfie**
AGE: **11**
OWNER: **Carolyn Armstrong**
PET LIKES: **Long walks at the beach, eating seaweed and tummy rubs**
PET HATES: **Cats and magpies**
HUMAN TRAITS: **He loves hugs and tries to talk by making a little whining noise**

8 **MONDAY**

9 **TUESDAY**

10 **WEDNESDAY**

11 **THURSDAY**

12 **FRIDAY**

13 **SATURDAY**

14 **SUNDAY**

All wound up

When I was about ten years old I set my heart on a book, The Royal Family, that I'd seen in the bookshop window. I was determined to have it and as it was the only copy I asked the owner, Mrs Gardener, to put it away until I could afford to buy it.

My plan was to earn the money by winding wool for my mother who knitted Fair Isle gloves for men, women and children. The different coloured wools were stacked in boxes in the hallway. We had a metal wool winder that had three adjustable arms. I was paid one penny pocket money for every ounce of wool that I wound.

One fine Saturday morning I placed a garden chair on the lawn, unfolded a card table and set the wool winder on it. That morning I wound 60 balls of brown wool (the main colour used in the gloves) and earned five shillings. Uncle George visited us in the afternoon and asked how many balls of wool I had wound.

When I told him he took five shillings from his pocket and said: "That's for being a good girl" – so I then had ten whole shillings!

Mum exchanged the coins for a ten-shilling note which I took to the bookshop. I told Mrs Gardener how I had earned the money and bought the book which I still have to this day. Following my mother's maxim of 'some to spend and some to save', I put the two shillings and sixpence change into my Post Office savings book.

Yvonne M Parsons, Exmouth

Top tip

The key to getting your cheapest supermarket basket yet? Look up! Supermarkets tend to place their most profitable stock at eye-level or at children's eye-level if it's for them, knowing you'll easily spot it and pop it in your basket. But if you look high and low, you may actually spot a much better deal.

Brain teaser

Fill the blank squares in this grid with digits so that each row, each column and each of the 3 x 3 blocks contains all the digits 1 to 9 once and once only.

		9		4		8		
1		5	7					
				1			3	
2				6			7	9
		8	2		3	1		
9	1			4				2
	8			5				
					9	7		6
	3		1		2			

My perfect pet

NAME: **Sasha**
AGE: **14**
OWNER: **Diana Wilson**
PET LIKES: **Crunching biscuits even though she only has six teeth and having prawns for a treat**
PET HATES: **Being cold**
HUMAN TRAITS: **She tries to communicate how she feels by looking straight into your eyes and making meow sounds**

Recipe of the week

COD WITH BROAD BEANS

Serves: 4
Preparation time: 15 mins
Cooking time: 8-10 mins

140g (5oz) pancetta cubes
4 sustainably sourced cod fillets
100g (3½oz) frozen or fresh peas
120ml (4floz) crème fraîche
4 tbsp basil pesto
150g (5oz) frozen or fresh broad beans, blanched and double podded
Chives, sliced on the diagonal
Steamed new potatoes to serve

1 Heat a frying pan. When hot, add the pancetta and cook for 5 mins until very crisp. Drain on kitchen paper and empty all but 1 tbsp of fat from the pan. Heat the grill to a medium high heat.

2 Oil the cod fillets lightly, season and place the fish on a grill rack. Grill for 8 to 10 mins, until moist and flaking. Meanwhile, warm the frying pan again, add the peas and crème fraîche and heat gently.

3 Stir through the pesto, then add the broad beans and the pancetta, check the seasoning and heat until the mixture is just beginning to steam. Serve the cod fillets with the sauce poured over, decorated with chives. Add a few steamed new potatoes that can be served alongside.
Credit: Sacla Italia

15 MONDAY

16 TUESDAY

17 WEDNESDAY

18 THURSDAY

19 FRIDAY

20 SATURDAY

21 SUNDAY

Memories are made of this

I could fill a book with memories of my childhood. We lived in Leighton Buzzard and the Grand Union Canal ran along the bottom of our garden. I used to watch the barges being pulled along by the horses on the towpath.

Every bargee had a bicycle on which he rode ahead to open the lock while his wife steered the boat through. The wives looked distinctive in their long cambric dresses worn underneath pinafores.

My father had an electrical business and the bargees used to bring their accumulators into the shop to have them charged up so they could listen to their radios. It cost sixpence a week to rent an accumulator.

I vividly remember the day that war was declared in September 1939. My family all sat around the radio listening to the Prime Minister's speech. Our two evacuees from London were also with us. They had arrived at the end of August. We even had our gas masks in their cardboard boxes ready on the table in front of us!

I have rather happier memories of a visit to my aunt a few years before this. She lived in Maida Vale in London and took me everywhere from the roof garden at Selfridge's to swimming with cousins at a nearby lido. When we went to London Zoo, I had rides on a pony, an elephant and even a camel. Sadly, I can't find the photo of me on an elephant, but I had a marvellous time!

Eileen Chapman, Luton

Animal magic

No wonder it's so hard to have an undisturbed picnic - it turns out there are 1,000,000 ants to every one human in the world. Anteaters, rejoice.

Top tip

You could bring down the price you pay on your petrol by making sure your tyre pressure is right. Have a look for the correct pressure for your car in the manual and test with a gauge or make the most of Halford's free tyre check. You'll also save at the pump by decluttering your car of any unnecessary junk you're storing in the boot and by turning the air-con off when driving at lower speeds.

Brain teaser

If the number in each circle is the sum of the two below it, how quickly can you work out the top number in each case?

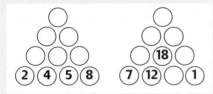

My perfect pet

NAME: **Brigadier (Briggy to his pals)**
AGE: **7**
OWNER: **Karen Hunton**
PET LIKES: **Cuddles, walks and travelling in the car**
PET HATES: **Going to the vets and next door's cat**
HUMAN TRAITS: **Sleeps on bed and snores. Enjoys wildlife programmes on TV**

Recipe of the week

YOGURT AND POPPYSEED CAKE

Makes: 1
Preparation time: 20 mins
Cooking time: 40 mins

175g (6oz) plain flour
Baking powder
75g (3oz) ground almonds
175g (6oz) caster sugar
150ml (5floz) natural set yogurt
75ml (3floz) corn oil
3 medium eggs
½ tsp of lemon extract
25g (1oz) poppy seeds
75g (3oz) white chocolate
150g (5oz) fresh mixed berries

1 Grease and line a 3lb loaf tin. Heat the oven to 180°C/350°F/Gas Mark 4. In a bowl, mix together the flour, baking powder, ground almonds and sugar until well combined.

2 In a jug, beat together the yogurt, oil, eggs and lemon extract. Make a well in the dry ingredients and pour in the egg mixture. Whisk all together until smooth, add the poppy seeds and stir to combine.

3 Pour into the prepared tin and bake for 40 mins until risen and firm. Leave to cool in the tin for a few mins, then transfer to a cooling rack to cool completely.

4 Melt the chocolate in a bowl over a simmering pan of water, decorate your cake with the berries and drizzle over the melted chocolate to finish it off.
Credit: Dr. Oetker

22 MONDAY

23 TUESDAY

24 WEDNESDAY

25 THURSDAY

26 FRIDAY

27 SATURDAY

28 SUNDAY

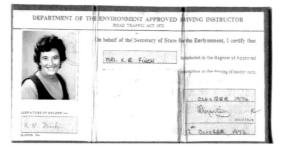

Put away those L-plates!

Although I didn't pass my driving test until I was 35, I followed my husband's example and went on to work as a driving instructor for 23 years. In that time, we experienced many hair-raising and sometimes amusing incidents as well as hundreds of happily uneventful lessons.

Once, when I was taking a young girl along a quiet country lane to practise stopping and starting, a car came racing towards us on the wrong side of the road. In a panic, she skidded across the grass verge and into a ditch. Luckily, a farmer came along on a tractor and pulled us out. We were covered in mud.

A young man who I took to Kettering for his driving test was late returning. The examiner walked back to tell me that someone had driven out of a junction and smashed into the car. As it wasn't his fault, he didn't fail the test but we had to return home in a pick-up truck.

Another time we took three generations for lessons. My husband taught the granddad while I taught the daughter and granddaughter. The only learner I ever felt nervous about was my son-in-law because his workmates teased him about his mother-in-law teaching him to drive - so I was very pleased when he passed first time.

I am 85 and retired but I still meet people who were once my pupils - although I often don't recognise them as they were youngsters when I knew them and they are now middle-aged!
Kath Finch, Market Harborough

Top tip

If you're not planning a holiday this year, make sure you drop any annual travel insurance you may be paying for as this is an unnecessary expense. With travel insurance, it's best to take it out once you book a holiday, start it up from then and cancel once your holiday is over.

Animal magic

Dolphins don't drink. Seawater would make them poorly, so instead they get all of their fluids through the food they eat.

Brain teaser

Can you identify four famous faces from the scramble pictures below?

My perfect pet

NAME: **Jessie**
AGE: **4**
OWNER: **Mary Green**
PET LIKES: **Butter licked off fingers and jumping in and out of windows – luckily she lives in a bungalow**
PET HATES: **Noise and passing traffic**
HUMAN TRAITS: **Loves eating toast with marmalade**

Recipe of the week

PEPPER AND SPINACH TART

Serves: 6
Preparation time: 10-20 mins
Cooking time: 30-35 mins

300g (11oz) plain flour
Pinch salt
125g (4½oz) trex/butter
For the filling:
300g (11oz) fresh spinach, washed
300g (11oz) roasted red peppers (from a jar)
2 x 210g (7½oz) packs mozzarella cheese sliced
3 eggs
300ml (½pt) pot crème fraîche
Basil leaves, to garnish

1 Sift the flour and salt into a large bowl. Add the Trex and rub until the mixture looks like fine crumbs. Stir in chilled water to make a soft, but not sticky dough. Knead then chill for 10-20 mins.

2 Preheat the oven to 200°C/400°F/Gas Mark 6. Roll out the pastry and line a 20x30cm (8x12in) oblong tart tin. Bake blind for 15 mins.

3 Take the flan from the oven and remove the baking beans. Reduce the temperature to 180°C/350°F/Gas Mark 4.

4 Wilt the spinach leaves in boiling water. Run cold water over, then squeeze the spinach to remove the excess water.

5 Tear the peppers into strips and arrange them in the case with the spinach and mozzarella. Beat the eggs and crème fraîche. Season. Pour into the case, then bake for 30-35 mins. Serve warm or cold.
Credit: Trex

29 **MONDAY**

30 **TUESDAY**

31 **WEDNESDAY**

1 **THURSDAY**

2 **FRIDAY**

3 **SATURDAY**

4 **SUNDAY**

That's my orange!

When I was just five years old (I am 73 now) in 1947, I was very anaemic, so I had to spend three long months in a children's hospital in Dawlish, Devon. I had just started school and I can remember clearly being fetched from school to be taken to the hospital.

At the hospital, they made me drink cabbage water every day as they said it was full of iron. Needless to say, to this day I do not like the taste of cabbage. We had lessons in the hospital and on the first day there I broke the lead in my pencil and got told off.

I got a telling off from the nurses one morning as well! We all had chamber pots under our beds which we were supposed to use at night. But one night I could not find mine so simply used the one under someone else's bed. What I didn't know was that they measured the amount passed each day!

My father had managed to get hold of a precious orange one time when my parents came to visit, but the nurses made me share it with the other children as they were so difficult to get hold of at that time. So I only got to taste one little segment of that orange and that memory has always stuck with me.

They did cure the anaemia though, thank goodness.

Molly Wright, Cambs

Top tip

Thinking about a July or August holiday abroad? Now's the time to book. 52 days ahead is thought to be the perfect time to get the cheapest flight deals - it's on average 26 per cent cheaper than booking on the day of departure. Tuesdays, early mornings and any evening after 6pm are also generally the cheapest times to fly, while Saturday is the most expensive.

Brain teaser

The symbols in this grid all represent a number between one and nine. When a symbol appears twice in a square it is doubled. The figure at the end of each row and column is the sum of the numbers in it. Can you work out which number each symbol represents?

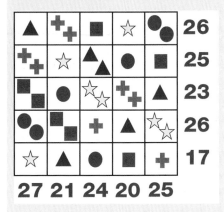

My perfect pet

NAME: **Dougy**
AGE: **8 months**
OWNER: **Lisa Lee**
PET LIKES: **Chewing everything, digging up the lawn and snuggling up with his best friend, Ollie the cat**
PET HATES: **Unwelcome visitors to his garden, especially neighbouring cats**
HUMAN TRAITS: **Collects post from the door and brings his owner's slippers to her when she gets home from work**

Recipe of the week

GRAPEFRUIT PAVLOVA

Makes: 1
Preparation time: 30 mins
Cooking time: 3 hours

For the meringue:
5 egg whites
300g (11oz) caster sugar
For the whipped cream topping:
300ml (½pt) double cream
1 tsp vanilla extract
1 tsp icing sugar
For the curd:
150ml (¼pt) grapefruit juice
50ml (2floz) lemon juice
75g (3oz) golden caster sugar
1 egg and 4 yolks
75g (3oz) unsalted butter
For the caramelised grapefruit:
2 grapefruits, thinly sliced
1 tbsp caster sugar

1 Preheat the oven to 200°C/400°F/Gas Mark 6. Line a deep tray and heat sugar in the oven for 5 mins. Whisk whites until they form stiff peaks. Reduce temperature to 120°C/248°/Gas Mark ½.

2 Add the sugar to the whites slowly. Whisk until stiff and glossy. Spread out in a 23cm (9in) circle on a lined baking tray and make a well. Cook for 2 hrs. Place the sliced grapefruit onto a tray and sprinkle with sugar. Place in the bottom part of the oven for 1-2 hrs. Cool the meringue for 1 hr.

3 Stir the juice, sugar and egg in a bowl over simmering water for 8-10 mins then remove and whisk in butter. Cover, cool, then chill till set. Whip cream, vanilla and icing sugar. Add the cream, curd, and dried grapefruit.
Credit: Florida Grapefruit

5 MONDAY

6 TUESDAY

7 WEDNESDAY

8 THURSDAY

9 FRIDAY

10 SATURDAY

11 SUNDAY

Hail, gales and a groom on drugs

Our wedding day, this day of days was made a little more memorable first, by the weather. As we arrived at the church, snow began to fall, it was icy cold and the wind was blowing a gale. This was followed by hailstones descending on us like concrete confetti. In the afternoon, the sun decided to put its hat on as we left the reception... We did not get married in the middle of winter, as you may think, but in midsummer – June 22, 1957! A guest at the wedding said that the weather was a reminder of how marriage was likely to be – a very mixed experience of bright days, but also of darker times. To everything there is a season, as it says in the Bible.

Secondly, we remember it well because the bridegroom had to limp up the aisle, hoping that he would not pass out before the ceremony was over. The night before, he had been doing some work at the little house that we had bought and were preparing for our life together. While moving some old floorboards outside, he dropped one and, unfortunately, it had a nail sticking out which he did not see. He trod on it and it went straight into his foot. He was taken to the doctor, where he had a tetanus jab and some painkillers. "Keep off the foot for 48 hours," he was told. "I can't do that," came the reply, "I'm getting married tomorrow." "In that case," said the doctor, "come to me before you go to the service and I will give you another injection that should see you through your day." And so he did.

Over the years, people sometimes asked my husband how he chose this quirky person (me) to be his wife. He would smile and say: "When I stood at the altar and said those two little words, 'I do', I'm afraid I said them while I was under the influence of drugs!" We will have been married 60 years in June, supporting each other in the bright days and the darker times. Every day we give thanks for the choice of partner that we made all those years ago.
Beryl Hartley, W Mids

Animal magic

There's a good reason you'll never spot a bat out for an afternoon constitutional – they can't walk, as the bones in their legs are too thin to support them.

Brain teaser

See if you can work out the answer to this problem:

Cinderella has found invites to Prince Charming's masked ball addressed to her two ugly sisters. Desperate to go, she dresses up and follows them, but is horrified to discover that a password is required to get in. The first sister steps up to the door and the guard says, 'twelve?' The sister replies with 'six' and is admitted to the party. 'Six?' the guard asks of the next sister, who answers 'three' and is also allowed in. Next up is Cinders and, when the doorman says 'nine', she grins and replies, 'four and a half', only to find herself being shoved down the steps where she nearly loses a glass slipper. Luckily, her Fairy Godmother appears at that precise moment and whispers the correct password into the girl's ear. She tells the guards who begrudgingly let her in. What is the password?

My perfect pet

NAME: **Blazey**
AGE: **10**
OWNER: **Jennifer Vieyra**
PET LIKES: **Cuddles and having his tummy rubbed**
PET HATES: **Other cats sharing his house. He keeps out of the way of their fights in another room**
HUMAN TRAITS: **Lying in his owner's arms like a baby**

Recipe of the week

CHICKEN WITH LIME AND MINT

Serves: 4
Preparation time: 15 mins
Cooking time: 20 mins

Juice of 2 limes
4 tbsp soy sauce
2 garlic cloves, peeled and crushed
2 tbsp clear honey
4 chicken breasts, skin on or removed as you prefer
2 tbsp groundnut oil
200g (7oz) dried rice noodles
1 tbsp chopped fresh mint, plus extra sprigs to garnish
½ cucumber, thinly sliced
1 large carrot, thinly sliced
1 red chilli, finely chopped

1 In a shallow dish mix together the lime juice, soy sauce, garlic and honey. Add the chicken breasts and baste. Set aside for 15 mins.

2 Heat the oil, add the chicken pieces to a pan. Cook over a medium heat until browned.

3 Turn the pieces over, lower the heat and pour in the marinade. Cover the pan and cook for 10 mins.

4 Uncover the pan and cook for 5 mins until the chicken is cooked through and the sauce has reduced and caramelised.

5 While the chicken is cooking, boil or soak the noodles in hot water.

6 Drain the noodles, toss them with the mint. Cut the chicken breasts into slices and arrange on top of the noodles with the cucumber and carrot. Scatter over the chilli and garnish with mint.
Credit: Kikkoman

12 MONDAY

13 TUESDAY

14 WEDNESDAY

15 THURSDAY

16 FRIDAY

17 SATURDAY

18 SUNDAY

Hi-jinks in hospital

In 1953, I was 15 years old, when a chest x-ray showed I had TB and I had to go into hospital. Because I was about to take my GCEs, they sent me to Harefield Hospital which had a school attached. After two-weeks isolation I was joined by some other teenage girls and our hospital life began. My brother brought in our Dansette record player and we played our favourites all evening until lights out at 7.30pm. Yes, we had to sit in darkness like little children. For the next 13 months we had a life similar to St Trinian's boarding school. Apart from Streptomycin injections in our legs every day, several other oral drugs, compulsory bedrest, a high calorie diet which included a raw egg in a glass of milk for our mid-morning snack, we had a good time.

We laughed, we acted out plays and we even made ourselves a cotton skirt each. We found out from our favourite staff nurse that there were some teenage boys on the men's ward just across the green from us and decided to visit. After lights out, we crawled along under Sister's office window, past the boy's ward and then climbed the wall around our enclosure. Then we ran as fast as we could across the grass and arrived breathless and laughing at the boy's cubicle. They played music while we sat on their beds and drank lemonade and dived under the beds if a nurse came along. After I went home, I heard from my best friend Bridie that she had got caught on the men's ward and expelled from the hospital. She must be the only patient to be expelled from a hospital ward. We are still good friends to this day.
Mary Archer, Middx

Top tip

It's the perfect time for a family picnic. Keep your hamper of food nice and cool by freezing cartons of drinks to use in your cool boxes or bags rather than buying ice blocks. It's cheaper, you'll have a refreshing iced drink to enjoy and it means you won't have to carry any heavy blocks around once you've finished.

Animal magic

You can tell what colour eggs a chicken will lay by looking at its ear lobes. A hen with red ear lobes will lay an egg with a brown shell, while those with white ear lobes will lay a white one!

Brain teaser

Fill the blank squares in this grid with digits so that each row, each column and each of the 3 x 3 blocks contains all the digits 1 to 9 once and once only.

	8		2					7
2			9			3		
4				1	6			
	4	6				8	5	
	9	3				4	6	
		8	7					9
	7			5				4
	5			4		1		

My perfect pet

NAME: **Merlin**
AGE: **9**
OWNER: **Tim Goodwin**
PET LIKES: **Sleeping on the sofa with the sunshine pouring through the French doors**
PET HATES: **Going for a walk in the rain**
HUMAN TRAITS: **Always does his best to keep cool on a hot day like wearing a damp t-shirt in a heat wave**

Recipe of the week

BLUEBERRY AND BANANA MUFFINS

Gluten Free

Makes: 12
Preparation time: 20 mins
Cooking time: 20 mins

75ml (2½oz) sunflower oil
1 medium over-ripe banana, mashed
200g (7oz) blueberries
1 lemon, zested
220ml (9floz) buttermilk
75g (3oz) light muscovado sugar
2 medium eggs
250g (9oz) gluten free self-raising flour
15g (½oz) gluten free baking powder
For the topping:
150g (5oz) quark
150g (5oz) cream cheese
5 tbsp icing sugar
1 tsp lemon extract
Dr. Oetker Madagascan Vanilla Grinder (for the topping)
15g (½oz) dried banana

1 Preheat the oven to 180°C/350°F/Gas Mark 4 and place the cupcake cases on a baking tray.

2 Mix the muscovado sugar and oil together until well mixed. Add the mashed banana, zest, buttermilk and egg to the sugar mix and beat.

3 Sift in the flour and mix until combined. Add the blueberries and fold in. Divide mixture between the cases.

4 Place in the oven and bake for 20 mins. Turn out onto cooling racks after 10 mins.

5 To top the muffins, take the quark and cream cheese straight from the fridge and mix together with sugar and lemon extract. Spread the desired amount over each muffin.

6 To finish, add a slice of dried banana and a couple of extra blueberries.
Credit: Dr. Oetker

19 MONDAY

20 TUESDAY

21 WEDNESDAY

22 THURSDAY

23 FRIDAY

24 SATURDAY

25 SUNDAY

My amazing mother

My dear mother was not well educated, in fact she taught herself to read aged 14 with the aid of film magazines and a little help from an uncle, who also encouraged her to smoke. Mum also learnt to play the piano by ear, although she could never read music. This enabled her to earn some extra money playing at weddings and parties, pubs and clubs. It was 'you hum it and I'll play it', and she did. She could tap dance and had a great voice that would challenge the likes of Sophie Tucker. Mum entertained in hospitals and the local theatres in Portsmouth and did a lot of charity work, but didn't make the big time.

She earned her living working in factories and cleaning in shops and pubs, jobs she hated doing. When the Second World War came she was lucky enough to get a job in Airspeed helping to make the wings of aeroplanes. She loved this job and did it so well she had a commendation from the Lord Mayor. She said she loved the war years as she had such a wonderful time, it was live for the day for her then, as she wasn't yet married and had no family to worry about. When the war was over she had to give her job at Airspeed up for the men returning from the forces and she was not pleased about that. She then had to take a job cleaning trains at Southern Railway Station in Fratton. Her luck changed when she met a lovely man called Fred travelling on the train, who soon became her husband and my father. The attached photo was taken when she worked on the trains, she is the tiny one in the front.

Valerie Reilly, Reading

Top tip

When you're on holiday, if you're asked if you'd like to pay in sterling or in the local currency, always choose the local currency. You'll get a much better exchange rate this way and so won't be paying over the odds on exactly the same items. Which means more money left over for holiday treats.

Animal magic

Guinea pigs need company to be happy – they aren't built to live alone. As a result, there's a law in Switzerland banning pet owners from keeping one by itself.

Brain teaser

All of the vowels have been removed from this completed crossword. Simply put them back where they belong, using only the vowels from the lists below. Remember to cross out each vowel as you place it in the grid, or you may well end up in a vowel mess!

AAAAAAA   EEEEEEEE
IIIIIIIII   OOOOOOOO   UUUU

My perfect pet

NAME: **Jemma**
AGE: **10**
OWNER: **Lynda Jacques**
PET LIKES: **Walks along the river in her new rain coat and being brushed**
PET HATES: **Having to be on a diet, which means no more biscuits**
HUMAN TRAITS: **Talking to anyone who comes to the door and watching TV**

Recipe of the week

MEDITERRANEAN CHICKEN AND VEGETABLES

Serves: 4
Preparation time: 20 mins
Cooking time: 45 mins

3 tbsp olive oil
1 red onion
1 courgette
1 yellow pepper
1 red pepper
1 aubergine
8 chicken thighs
1 tbsp chopped fresh thyme
3 tbsp soy sauce
200ml (7floz) chicken stock
4 tbsp tomato pasta sauce

1 Put the olive oil in a large bowl. Peel and cut the onion into wedges, trim and chop the courgette into bite-size pieces. Remove the stalks from the peppers and the aubergine. Deseed the peppers, cut them, and the aubergine, into small, bite-sized chunks.

2 Add the vegetables to the bowl and stir until they are coated with the oil. Spoon them into a large roasting tin, spreading them out evenly.

3 Tuck the chicken thighs among the vegetables and sprinkle with the chopped thyme.

4 Preheat the oven to 180°C/350°F/Gas Mark 4. Roast the chicken and vegetables for 30 mins.

5 Mix together the soy sauce, chicken stock and pasta sauce and pour into the pan over the vegetables and around the chicken pieces. Return to the oven for a further 15-20 mins or until the chicken is cooked through and the vegetables are tender.
Credit: Kikkoman

26 MONDAY

27 TUESDAY

28 WEDNESDAY

29 THURSDAY

30 FRIDAY

1 SATURDAY

2 SUNDAY

Blast from the past

Well, fancy that!

For fifty years
I attended the
Hampton Road
United Reformed
Church in Southport
before it closed
seven years ago
owing to a dwindling
congregation. I taught
at the Sunday School
and also acted as
treasurer for a while.

When I was the
social secretary I used to organise holidays for our
church fellowship and we had some wonderful
times in destinations as far apart as Bournemouth
and Dundee.

This photo was taken of me with a friend when we
were on one of these holidays in the early Seventies.
We had plucked up the courage to enter the hotel's
fancy dress competition. My friend donned a dressing
gown, borrowed a doll and described herself as 'Left
Holding the Baby'. I asked the barman for some empty
drink bottles, borrowed some sheets from the bed and
went as 'Departed Spirits'. To our amazement, we were
awarded the first and second prize!

Although I would describe myself as quite a
reserved person, life has put me in the spotlight
from time to time. A colleague who was a member
of our local amateur dramatic society bullied me into
auditioning for their production of The Sound of
Music. To my amazement I got the part and ended up
playing Sister Berthe.

These days, despite my family's pleas to sit back
and take life easy, I sit on two committees and also
belong to my church choir. I have found that willing
volunteers are always needed.

Helen Connolly, Southport

Top tip

In the supermarket, if a special offer item you
wanted is out of stock, you may able to get a
compensation voucher. ASDA staff can give
away 'Smiley Vouchers' worth up to £1 when
something's not right, including if an item is out
of stock. Meanwhile, Sainsbury's can give out
coupons allowing you to buy the same product
from a different brand at the special offer price.
It's at the staff member's discretion, though, so
be sure to ask politely.

Brain teaser

Insert letters into the grid to form seven words reading across. When you have finished, the name of a celebrity will be spelt out reading down the yellow squares.

C	A		O		Y
S	H		D		W
F	U		U		E
Q	U		R		Z
S	O		E		N
A	N		M		L
C	L		A		S

Recipe of the week

MOZZARELLA AND BASIL QUICHE

Serves: 4
Preparation time: 10 mins
Cooking time: 30-35 mins

175g (6oz) plain flour
100g (3½oz) butter
3 tsp cold water
210g (7½oz) pack mozzarella, drained
75g (3oz) sun blushed tomatoes, drained and chopped
Large handful basil leaves
50g (2oz) parmesan cheese, grated
300ml (½pt) milk
4 medium eggs
Salt and pepper to taste

1 Preheat the oven to 200°C/400°F/Gas Mark 6 and grease the quiche dish with butter or oil. Rub the butter into the flour till the mixture resembles fine breadcrumbs and then add enough water to form a dough. Roll this dough out on a floured surface and then use it to line the quiche dish.

2 Put the mozzarella, tomatoes and basil into the pastry case with half of the Parmesan.

3 Beat the milk and eggs together and season with salt and pepper. Pour the egg mixture through a sieve over the filling and top the quiche with the remaining cheese.

4 Bake in the oven for 30-35 mins until golden brown and set. Take out of the oven and leave to cool in the quiche dish, or slice and serve warm with a salad and new potatoes.
Credit: Pyrex

My perfect pet

NAME: **Pippa**
AGE: **10 months**
OWNER: **Jean McHugh**
PET LIKES: **Going for long walks, playing with her friends and attending puppy classes**
PET HATES: **Being away from her owner**
HUMAN TRAITS: **Taps her water bowl if it's empty and goes round shutting open doors**

3 MONDAY

4 TUESDAY

5 WEDNESDAY

6 THURSDAY

7 FRIDAY

8 SATURDAY

9 SUNDAY

Schoolgirls' sewing bee

St Wilfrid's, the school I attended in Exeter, was run by a community of nuns and we were taught to be mindful of other people's needs. When I was aged 12, Sister Elsie gave a talk to our class on the plight of lepers overseas. The disease had a devastating effect on its victims who were forced to live in isolated colonies as it was very contagious. We were shocked to learn that leprosy caused sufferers to lose their fingers and toes.

Sister Elsie suggested that some of us might like to volunteer to form a sewing group that would stay on after classes were over to blanket stitch things such as flannels and sew some cotton items. The idea was to sell them at a sale of works to raise money for the lepers.

I became one of the group who, with our parents' permission, happily stayed on to sew after school. It was rewarding to see the results, even though our fingers were often pricked by the needles. I, for one, could never learn to use a thimble!

At the end of term a sale was held at the Rougemont Hotel in Queen Street. We were cordially invited to attend and it was exciting to see our sewn items on display for sale as well as knowing that the money raised would help the lepers.

It is good to know that today there are more effective treatments for this cruel disease than was the case back in 1952.

Sheila Mills, Minehead

Top tip

If you buy a new bottle of water each week or even more often than that, it's time to rethink your habits. Not only is it bad for the environment, it's also a drain on your purse. Ironically, tap water is generally cleaner and so better for you than bottled water, anyway. So invest in a good reusable bottle and just refill from the tap each time.

Animal magic

Sea sponges have no head, brain, heart, lungs, mouth, eyes, bones or feelers, yet they are still living creatures... if not the most engaging dinner party guests.

Brain teaser

It's that time again for the yearly visit to the beach and it looks like there's more than enough going on to keep everyone entertained! There are at least 10 objects in this picture starting with the letter M. How many can you find?

My perfect pet

NAME: **Boo**
AGE: **3**
OWNER: **Jan Day**
PET LIKES: **Chicken, carrots, runner beans and walks on the beach**
PET HATES: **Puddles and big dogs**
HUMAN TRAITS: **Sleeping on the bed**

Recipe of the week

BACON AVOCADO BURGER

Serves: 4
Preparation time: 20 mins
Cooking time: 10 mins

400g (14oz) lean beef mince
4 lean bacon rashers
2 tomatoes
1 small red onion
4 burger buns
2 tbsp mayo
1 ripe avocado
½ lime
A grind of black pepper and sea salt

1 Place the minced beef in a medium-sized bowl, season with pepper and mix well. Divide into 4 evenly sized balls and flatten into burger shapes. Place in the fridge to chill.

2 Cut the avocado in half, remove the stone and scoop out the flesh and chop into small cubes.

3 Place the avocado in a bowl, then add the mayonnaise, lime zest and juice, season with pepper and mix well. Taste to see if the seasoning needs adjusting at all.

4 Preheat a griddle pan or BBQ.

5 Cook the burgers for 3 to 4 mins on each side, or to your liking. Once cooked remove and keep in a warm place. Now cook the bacon for 1 min on both sides, until crispy.

6 Place the burgers in the buns, top with sliced tomatoes and sliced onions, then the avocado mayonnaise and finish with the crispy bacon and serve.
Credit: www.hellmanns.co.uk

10 MONDAY

11 TUESDAY

12 WEDNESDAY

13 THURSDAY

14 FRIDAY

15 SATURDAY

16 SUNDAY

Stupid contest!

I grew up on the Isle of Wight and the summer that my friend Mandy and I were 14 years old, we tried to earn ourselves some money by entering the Bembridge Holiday Princess contest, even though we weren't on holiday, as we were local.

It was being judged by Arthur Lowe, who played Captain Mainwaring from Dad's Army and there was a promise of cash prizes. He was a very big star as the show was huge on telly back then - plus at 14 some extra money was always useful. We couldn't wait.

We caught the bus from Ryde and when we got to Bembridge found that so many girls had turned up that there would be two rounds. Everyone was given a number and Round One consisted of simply walking across the stage. As it took forever and they were running out of time, the organisers said they would pick ten numbers at random out of a hat and those picked would go through to the final round. What a total fiasco. These so-called 'finalists' were the only ones who got to meet the Dad's Army star.

Neither Mandy nor I had our numbers picked. We hadn't really expected to win but we felt pretty fed up on the way home because we'd paid out for buses - and so had actually lost money on the day and in the end it hadn't been a fair contest.

Lorraine Cooke, Southampton

Supermarkets typically display reduced prices on foods with imminent sell-by dates from around 10am onwards each day. The foods with serious price reduction then go out from around 7pm. Visit your store at different times of day to see when the best bargain foods are about. And if you spot an item about to go out of date or that's damaged on the normal shelves, always politely ask if you might be able to have a discount.

Brain teaser

Here's one to drive you up the wall. Enter the solutions to the clues in their numbered layers of the wall. Each word must be an anagram of its neighbours, plus or minus one letter.

1 Disease also known as lockjaw
2 Teases, torments
3 Spectacular act to gain publicity
4 Crazy, bonkers
5 The - - -, tabloid newspaper
6 Responsibility, burden
7 Animal's nose
8 Every Second - - -, 1980s game show with Paul Daniels
9 Refer to for information

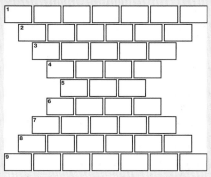

My perfect pet

NAME: **Ellie**
AGE: **5**
OWNER: **Jo and Peter Bronner**
PET LIKES: **Paper bags to play in and destroy and scratching the garden fence**
PET HATES: **Other cats visiting her garden and fireworks**
HUMAN TRAITS: **Always 'chatting' and is very nosey – she likes to know what's going on**

Recipe of the week

SUNDAE SEMIFREDDO

Serves: 10
Preparation time: 25 mins
Freezing time: 3 hrs

250g (9oz) chocolate truffles
Olive oil for the tin
75g (3oz) golden caster sugar
4 medium free-range eggs
450ml (¾pt) double cream

1 Lightly oil and line a 900g (2lb) loaf tin with cling film, this will make it easier for the semifreddo to slip out.

2 Put the sugar and eggs in a heatproof bowl, then place over a pan of simmering water and whisk until pale, thick and almost doubled in volume.

3 Remove from the heat and place the bowl into cold water, continuing to whisk until the mixture is cool. Meanwhile, melt the chocolate in another bowl over the pan of hot water then stir the mixture and fold into the egg.

4 Whip the cream to soft peaks and fold in to the chocolate and egg mixture. Pour the mixture in to the loaf tin and smooth the surface with a palette knife, then cover and freeze until firm or 3 hrs. To serve, turn out and remove the cling film, then using a sharp knife, cut thick slices on to serving plates. Drizzle over raspberry coulis and add some fresh raspberries.
Credit: Divine Chocolate

17 MONDAY

18 TUESDAY

19 WEDNESDAY

20 THURSDAY

21 FRIDAY

22 SATURDAY

23 SUNDAY

Sounds of the Seventies

After I started work as a clerk typist in July 1979, my first major purchase was this Fidelity record player with speakers. I earned all of £30 a week and it took me four months to save the £79 I needed to buy it from the Norwich Co-op's electrical department.

I played my small collection of LPs over and over again. The Sound of Bread and Simon and Garfunkel's Greatest Hits were the background music to my years of teenage angst. When I felt upbeat I played The Monkees, The Searchers or the Everly Brothers and when I felt rebellious I played Hazel O'Connor. Next to the record player, there is a disco light with a revolving plastic disc that flashed different colours on my lime-green walls as I danced around my bedroom to the sound of The Beatles or Blondie.

Please note the blue and purple floral design curtains - and yes, there was a matching bedspread! The décor included a poster of The Police as well as one of the Liverpool football team (an advertisement for milk!)

Eventually, when I was in my early 20s, I bought a radio/cassette player to replace the record player which I passed on to my Nan who used it for many years to play her favourite Ken Dodd album. Retail therapy was unheard of in those days but I feel I certainly got value from my first 'big ticket' purchase.
S B Ingle, Norwich

Top tip

Fancy a new hair-do for your summer holidays? Save money by letting a student cut your hair. Most students will have had plenty of training and will always have a teacher right beside them, so there's very little chance of things going wrong, and they'll often do your cut for a bargain price - or in some cases, for free. Certain Toni & Guy and Vidal Sassoon hair salons have specific slots when you can get a student cut.

Animal magic

Jellyfish have been on the planet for more than 650 million years, making them older (and tougher) than the dinosaurs. We'll never feel old again!

Brain teaser

Fill the blank squares in this grid with digits so that each row, each column and each of the 3 x 3 blocks contains all the digits 1 to 9 once and once only.

	6					1		
	3		4	6			2	8
9					7			
		1	2		4		5	
	2						1	
	7		3		8	6		
			5					4
2	9			4	3		6	
		8					9	

My perfect pet

NAME: **Ted**
AGE: **3**
OWNER: **Amy Mannifield**
PET LIKES: **Chocolate éclairs (without the chocolate) and being wrapped up in a blanket**
PET HATES: **The rain and the dark**
HUMAN TRAITS: **He shares everything, except his own stuff**

Recipe of the week

LEMON AND COURGETTE CUPCAKES

Serves: 12
Preparation time: 25 mins
Cooking time: 25 mins

175g (6oz) plain flour
1 tsp baking powder
115g (4oz) sugar
150g (5oz) courgette
2 medium eggs, beaten
4 tbsp of oil
1 tsp of lemon extract
To decorate:
200g (7oz) light cream cheese
2 (tbsp) icing sugar
1 tsp of vanilla extract
Lemon zest

1 Preheat the oven to 180°C/350°F/Gas Mark 4. Line a fairy cake tin with 12 baking cases. Sift the flour and baking powder into a bowl and stir in the sugar. Make a well in the centre of the mixture and add the courgette, eggs, oil and extract. Mix until combined.

2 Divide the mixture between the baking cases and bake for about 25 mins until risen, lightly golden and firm to the touch. Cool and store in an airtight container for 24 hrs to allow the flavour and texture to develop.

3 To decorate: put the soft cheese in a bowl and beat with a wooden spoon to soften. Sift the icing sugar on top and add the vanilla extract. Mix together until well blended.

4 Spread a little soft cheese topping over each cake and sprinkle with lemon zest.
Credit: Dr. Oetker

24 MONDAY

25 TUESDAY

26 WEDNESDAY

27 THURSDAY

28 FRIDAY

29 SATURDAY

30 SUNDAY

Just not fair

Back in 1950, when I was seven, having my tonsils out was a trauma and a half. My family doctor had held back referring me until a surgeon nicknamed 'the butcher' had gone on holiday.

My mother had to leave me at the hospital on a Sunday and come back for me on the following Tuesday. The operations were carried out on the Monday and a whole group of us children, wrapped in blankets, were wheeled down to theatre on a communal trolley. From the ante-room I could hear the children being asked to start counting and most were under anaesthetic by the count of four. When it came to my turn I was given the same instruction. I got to 33 and remember the look in the surgeon's eyes as the nurse pushed on my stomach to make me take in more of the gas.

When I came round, early, because I hadn't taken much gas, I was back in the ward in my bed. I was lying on a grubby rubber sheet with an enamel bowl of blood at the side of me. Mary in the next bed had had her operation the day before and was sleeping under beautiful white sheets and blankets. I croakily called a nurse and asked why I wasn't in that sort of a bed. She said: "You shouldn't have woken up so soon! If you don't behave I'll fetch the doctor." After reflecting on this for a few moments I felt the first stirrings of trade unionism. Despite my burning and bleeding throat, I got up, stuck the bowl and the rubber sheet under my bed and deftly whipped a blanket off Mary's bed. She didn't even wake up.

Wendy Haynes, Derbys

Top tip

If you're a Tesco shopper, make sure you're aware of Tesco Clubcard Boost, where you can trade up your points to be worth three or four times more than they are in-store. For example, a 500-point voucher is worth a fiver in Tesco but could be worth £15-£20 on Tesco Clubcard Boost, which you can then spend on days out, travel cards, meals out and more.

Animal magic

If you thought humans were the only species with a 'women and children first' policy, think again. While many animals have a dog-eat-dog mentality, raccoons are more respectful - backing down to allow mothers and babies to eat first.

Brain teaser

Use the letters from the words below to form six five-letter words to fit the grid. Three letters have been placed and the clue to the first word reading across is Diaper

DRINK   FADE   LAZY   NEAR   PIPE

My perfect pet

NAME: **Chutney Chipmunk**
AGE: **11**
OWNER: **Nicky Brownhill**
PET LIKES: **Eating monkey nuts, sunbathing, hiding food and generally being very inquisitive**
PET HATES: **Loud noises, cats, dogs and magpies**
HUMAN TRAITS: **Holding her food in her hands and eating very daintily**

Recipe of the week

Gluten Free

GREEK POTATO SALAD

Serves: 4-5
Preparation time: 10 mins
Cooking time: 10-15 mins

10 medium Maris Piper potatoes
1 red onion
3-4 tbsp mini capers
150g (5oz) feta cheese, cubed
Handful parsley, finely chopped
½ tsp dried oregano
1 lemon, juiced
Salt and freshly ground black pepper
Plenty of extra virgin olive oil

1 Peel the potatoes and then cut them into quarters. Fill a medium pot with water, add the potatoes and a good pinch of salt and bring to the boil. Lower heat to a simmer and cook until the potatoes are just fork tender. Drain and leave to cool slightly and transfer to a platter or large bowl.

2 Scatter the capers and feta over the potatoes. Sprinkle the dish with the chopped parsley and dried oregano. Season with salt and freshly ground black pepper.

3 Use a mandolin or very sharp knife to slice the onion as thinly as possible. Scatter the onions and a squeeze the lemon over the salad. Drizzle with plenty of olive oil and serve immediately.
Credit: Ao.com/life

31 MONDAY

1 TUESDAY

2 WEDNESDAY

3 THURSDAY

4 FRIDAY

5 SATURDAY

6 SUNDAY

The winner is...

It seems to me that when I was growing up there were always fancy dress competitions going on. And back then, unlike today, most of the costumes were fashioned out of stuff that was lying about at home and put together by our ingenious mothers and fathers. In this photo I was four or five years old, so it would have been 1955 or 1956. I am the one on the far right with a cardboard placard around my neck which reads, 'no more strikes'. My outfit consisted of a dress made out of some old blackout material, which was covered with spent matchsticks - they were plentiful back then due to smoking and gas cookers and fires which needed to be lit. On my head I had empty matchboxes attached to a black band. My older sister was next to me and she had a doll's pram full of dolls as she was the nursery rhyme, 'There was an old woman who lived in a shoe'.

The competition was at a fête in Leominster and I can still remember my delight when I won first prize. This consisted of three ten-shilling notes - which was a tidy sum back then. I can still picture opening the envelope and taking out the three crisp, red notes and then running up, so pleased, to show my father.

We went to a lot of fêtes and country shows with my mum and dad in those days. An ice-cream was still a big treat then, so that was always the highlight of any visit for me.

Jennifer Phillipson, Hereford

Top tip

Knowing the difference between food labels could save you a lot of waste. 'Use-by' date is the one you want to pay attention to as this means food should be thrown after this date or it's a health risk. 'Best before', though, means food is usually okay to eat after the date but it might not be at its very best. Use your own judgment on this one. Ignore 'display-until' and 'sell-by' dates – these are instructions for shop staff, not you.

Animal magic

Are you a perfume fanatic? You're in good company – it turns out that many big cats go crazy for Calvin Klein's Obsession For Men. So much so that many photographers spray it on their camera traps to attract them.

Brain teaser

Each row and column in the grid should contain one each of the letters A, B, C, D and one blank square. A letter beside a row or column indicates the first of the four letters encountered when going in the direction of the arrow. Your task is to fit the letters into the grid.

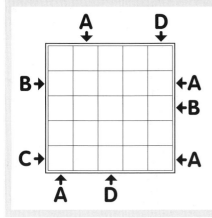

My perfect pet

NAME: **Trixie**
AGE: **3**
OWNER: **Linda Lewis**
PET LIKES: **Biscuits (the ones humans like) and chasing her tail**
PET HATES: **Next door's cat**
HUMAN TRAITS: **She hates being ignored and sits in her owner's office chair to stop her from working**

Recipe of the week

PASSION FRUIT AND PISTACHIO CAKE

Serves: 10
Preparation time: 15 mins
Cooking time: 50 mins

250g (9oz) butter
250g (9oz) sugar
100g (3½oz) pistachios, roasted
100g (3½oz) ground almonds
200g (7oz) plain flour
1 tsp baking powder
2 tbsp yogurt
3 eggs
1 orange, zested and juiced
For the icing:
50g (2oz) butter, room temperature
150g (5oz) cream cheese
75g (3oz) icing sugar
1 passion fruit (or passion fruit curd)
1 tbsp granola

1 Butter and line a 20cm (8in) cake tin. Preheat oven to 180°C/350°F/Gas Mark 4.

2 Mix the butter and sugar. After 3 mins, add pistachios, almonds, flour, baking powder and the yogurt. Beat till mixed. Add the eggs one at a time.

3 Pour the batter into the cake tin and cook for 50 mins, until a skewer comes out clean. Leave to cool.

4 Whisk the sugar and the butter until pale. Add the cream cheese, then whisk in the icing sugar. Halve the passion fruit then sieve the juice into the icing. You could add the seeds, but the juice will do (or a tbsp of passion fruit curd). Stir and then spread over the icing. Crumble the granola over the top for a crunch.
Credit: www.lizis.co.uk

7 MONDAY

8 TUESDAY

9 WEDNESDAY

10 THURSDAY

11 FRIDAY

12 SATURDAY

13 SUNDAY

Flat irons and gas mantles

I spent a lot of time at my Granny Amy's cottage when I was a little girl. I lived there for my first four years of life because my dad was in the air force. Then I couldn't keep away in later years because there was always lots of family coming and going and it was just so homely and welcoming. There was no electricity, just a gas stove in the pantry, gas mantle lamps and a tap outside. But there was always a lovely coal fire in a big black range.

To get to the garden you had to climb up 20 sandstone steps and halfway up there was always a bed of yellow celandines in spring time. I still love these flowers and have them in my garden today. Granny and Granddad's garden was always full of vegetables - which, freshly picked from the ground, tasted completely different to anything you get from the shops. It gave me an early love for vegetables that I've never lost.

On Saturday afternoon a van would pull up outside the front door and Granny would do her shopping. I remember she would always let me pull the coupons out of the ration book and afterwards I could have a few sweets.

We finished Saturdays off with cleaning the cutlery and doing some ironing - using flat irons heated on the range. I will always look back with so many happy memories of Granny Amy's lovely, homely cottage.
Janette Young, Worcs

Top tip

Giving your house a good clean needn't involve forking out for expensive cleaning products. One of the best cleaners around is probably already in your fridge. Mix a little grated lemon rind with water to form a liquid and keep this in a recycled container to use on your worktops, in the fridge, in your wheelie bins, anywhere that needs a clean. If you need to give something a deep scrub, try adding bicarbonate of soda.

Animal magic

Ever wondered how camels keep the sand out of their eyes? Nature has provided them with a whopping three pairs of eyelids! It must be a nightmare taking a nice photo without them blinking.

Brain teaser

In this puzzle, each symbol stands for a whole number between one and nine. The number at the end of each row and column equals the sum of the numbers in it. When a symbol appears twice in a square it is doubled. Can you work out which number each symbol represents?

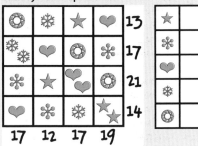

Recipe of the week

LAMB AND APRICOT BURGERS

Serves: 4-6
Preparation time: 5-10 mins
Cooking time: 8-12 mins

450g (1lb) lean Welsh lamb mince
1 tsp oil
1 small onion, peeled and finely sliced
1 tsp mild curry powder
50g (2oz) dried apricots, roughly chopped.

1 Heat the oil in a small pan and lightly cook onions until they become translucent and a little brown around the edges. Add in the curry powder and fry for 1-2 mins. Allow the onions to cool.

2 Place the mince and apricots into a bowl and add in the cooled onions. Using your hands, mix everything together and season the mixture.

3 Divide the mixture into 4 or 6 and shape the balls into burgers. Place the burgers on a plate that has been covered with greaseproof paper so they don't stick when you go to place them on the grill or the barbecue.

4 Place under a preheated grill or on a hot barbecue for 8-12 mins, turning the burgers occasionally until the meat is cooked through. Check whether they're done by sticking a skewer into the middle and checking the juices are clear.

5 Serve the burgers up with curried mayo and spicy couscous.

Credit: www.eatwelshlambandwelshbeef.com/en

My perfect pet

NAME: **Harvey**
AGE: **12**
OWNER: **Sonia Rowbotham**
PET LIKES: **Anything that's edible and chasing a bottle at the beach**
PET HATES: **When it's home time – he goes into a mood and refuses to walk until he gets his own way**
HUMAN TRAITS: **Doesn't want to go out when it's raining**

14 MONDAY

15 TUESDAY

16 WEDNESDAY

17 THURSDAY

18 FRIDAY

19 SATURDAY

20 SUNDAY

Driven crazy

One time, when I took my driving test (yes, there was more than one) my husband drove me there in the pouring rain. I told him not to park too near to the car in front so it wouldn't be too hard for me to drive away. When the examiner asked if I could read the number plate on the car he was pointing to, I said I should be able to because it was my car. He then told me to get settled comfortably in my car. I did but, unfortunately, I trapped my coat in the door. Because there was a fault with my door, I didn't want to open it again and I couldn't reach the other door to open it for the examiner.

I left him standing there in the pouring rain while I tried to slither out of my coat. Eventually he got in but by this time his sheet of paper was wet through.

After a few attempts to start the car we set off. The examiner told me to turn left, but we ended up in a pub car park. He said he'd love a whisky, but not during the test! Needless to say I didn't pass that time.

Subsequently, I booked an hour's driving lesson before my next test. However, the instructor didn't arrive. I telephoned and they rang to wake him up. They said there was still time to make the test and I walked into the room just as the examiner was calling out my name. I simply didn't have time to feel nervous so I finally passed.

Catherine Snowden, Gt Manchester

Top tip

If you're an online shopper, there's a clever trick you can do to try to bag yourself a discount. Sign in, set up your order and add just a couple of things into your basket and then quit your order before paying. Sometimes, supermarkets will then email you asking why you didn't complete your order and offer you a discount voucher as a way to entice you back.

Animal magic

Parrots aren't just pretty pollies - they can solve certain word puzzles as quickly as a 6-year-old child, grasping concepts such as 'same', 'different', 'bigger' and 'smaller'. Who's a clever boy, then?

Brain teaser

See if you can work out the answer to this problem?

Three men go to a café and order a meal, the total cost of which is £15. They each contribute £5 to pay the bill. The waiter takes the money to the chef who recognises the three men as friends and asks the waiter to return £5 to them.

The waiter is not only poor at maths but also dishonest and instead of going to the trouble of splitting the £5 between the three men he simply gives them £1 each and pockets the remaining £2 for himself.

Now, each of the men effectively paid £4, so the total paid is therefore £12. Add the £2 in the waiter's pocket and this comes to £14. So where has the other £1 gone from the original £15?

My perfect pet

NAME: **Poppy**
AGE: **3**
OWNER: **Linda Catton**
PET LIKES: **Playing with tiny tennis balls and going for walks**
PET HATES: **Squirrels, wood pigeons and anything else that happens to be in 'her' garden**
HUMAN TRAITS: **Loves sleeping on mum's bed**

Recipe of the week

SMOOTHIE BOWL

Serves: 2
Preparation: 5 mins

For the base:
200g (7oz) frozen berries (blueberries, raspberries, blackberries, strawberries)
100g (3½oz) frozen, sliced banana
2 heaped tbsp porridge oats
300-350ml (½pt) almond milk, oat milk or cow's milk
2 tbsp clear honey
4 tbsp plain yogurt
2 tbsp almond butter
For the toppings:
Frozen or fresh berries (blueberries, raspberries, blackberries, strawberries)
Almonds or pumpkin seeds
Desiccated coconut, goji berries and extra runny honey

1 Put all of the smoothie ingredients into a blender with 300ml (½pt) of the milk and then blitz on high until you have a smooth, thick consistency, adding more milk if needed; the smoothie should be thick enough to eat with a spoon, so don't add too much liquid.

2 Pour the smoothie mixture into two bowls and sprinkle the bowls with toppings of your choice, adding in a drizzle of runny honey. Eat the smoothie bowls straight away while still icy cold.

3 If you want, fill ice-lolly trays up with the smoothie mixture. Stick a wooden stick in the centre of each one before freezing for 2 hrs or more depending on your freezer.
Credit: Rowse Honey

21 MONDAY

22 TUESDAY

23 WEDNESDAY

24 THURSDAY

25 FRIDAY

26 SATURDAY

27 SUNDAY

Not the best start

I got married on September 5, 1964 to my fiancé Alan. The day started with a telephone call from the florist saying there was a problem with the flowers I had ordered and could I call in? After sorting the problem out I returned home, and was getting ready for the ceremony, when I cut my thumb on a razor, which necessitated wearing a plaster on my right thumb (you can actually see it in some of the photos). There were two cars ordered - one for me and my dad and one for the bridesmaid and page boy. But only one car actually turned up, so our next-door neighbour, Mr West, kindly put on a decent jacket over his work clothes and took Dad and me to the church. The vicar had previously warned us that if, for any reason, I should be late, he would be unable to marry us as he had a very tight schedule and no marriages could be performed after 5pm. I rushed out of our neighbour's car to see the vicar waiting on the steps of the church. We'd made it. We were married and went to Belgium for our honeymoon.

We arrived at our hotel at about 2am having caught the night ferry from Dover. It turned out Alan had booked the hotel for Sunday September 6 - so we spent our wedding night in the hotel lounge. Also, when we had been sorting out our luggage before leaving we, inadvertently, left most of our money behind and only had just enough to pay the bill at the end of the week. We phoned home and were sent some, thankfully. But despite our dodgy start 52 years later we are still very happy.
Geraldine Verrills, Surrey

Top tip

For a cheaper bottle of wine look for bottles from lesser-known countries. Wines that have a reputation already, such as French Sauvignon Blanc or Italian Pinot Grigio, are easy to sell, but unusual wines from Turkey, Romania or Slovenia, for example, have to be really good to get on a supermarket's shelves and they tend to be cheaper because they can't command high prices.

Animal magic

The temperature at which an Australian saltwater crocodile keeps its eggs will determine the gender of its babies. Eggs incubated below 30°C will hatch females, while warmer temperatures result in males.

Brain teaser

Fill the blank squares in this grid with digits so that each row, each column and each of the 3 x 3 blocks contains all the digits 1 to 9 once and once only.

3			4				2	7
		8						
9	7		2			4	8	
	2	5			7			3
8			5			9	1	
	1	3		4			6	9
				9				
4	6			5			3	

My perfect pet

NAME: **Sherringham Shez**
AGE: **15**
OWNER: **Sandrea Brown**
PET LIKES: **Cuddles and sitting on knees**
PET HATES: **Cats**
HUMAN TRAITS: **He helps with the sewing and keeps asking for food until he gets some**

Recipe of the week

MUSHROOM AND PARMESAN TART

Serves: 4
Preparation time: 40 mins
Cooking time: 22 mins

50g (2oz) plain flour, and a handful for dusting
2 large eggs, beaten
25g (1oz) butter
300g (11oz) mushrooms of your choice sliced
25g (1oz) finely shaved vegetarian parmesan
Small handful of chopped parsley leaves
1 garlic clove finely chopped

1 In a bowl, stir the flour, sugar and salt. Add the butter, then the egg mixture and mix until the dough comes together. Transfer to a work surface and flatten into a disk. Wrap in cling film and refrigerate for about 30 mins.

2 Heat oven to 190°C/375°F/Gas Mark 5. On a lightly floured surface, roll out the pastry into a circle, roughly 10x12cm. Transfer to a parchment-lined baking sheet.

3 Using a knife, score a 1in border around the pastry. Brush the border with egg mixture. Bake until golden brown and puffed, 18-22 mins.

4 Heat a pan until hot, add butter and fry the mushrooms for around 5 mins. Season then remove the pan from the heat and mix the mushrooms with the parmesan cheese, parsley and garlic.

5 Rescore the border of the cooked pastry and flatten it down. Spoon the mushroom mixture into the middle.

Credit: udisglutenfree.co.uk/

28 MONDAY

29 TUESDAY

30 WEDNESDAY

31 THURSDAY

1 FRIDAY

2 SATURDAY

3 SUNDAY

Mighty Maxie

My cat Amy had a litter of kittens and one day decided to move them. I don't know how she did it, but she climbed to the top of a chest of drawers and made a new home on an old jumper. The last kitten she moved, she dropped, and the first I knew of it was a continuous wailing and screaming from the tiny kitten.

He was trying to crawl but his back legs just trailed behind him. I took him to my very kindly vet, who said that it would be best to put him to sleep as he had damaged his spine and his legs were paralysed. But do you know that tiny kitten put a paw on my hand, started to purr and looked up at us so beseechingly, we couldn't do it. My vet put his little legs in tiny splints and when bandaged it looked as if he was wearing moon boots.

We called him Maximilian as he was so brave. He had to have his dressings changed frequently and he learned to trundle happily after his siblings, although not able to run quickly or jump as they could. When his dressings were finally removed, his feet were deformed but he was amazingly able to run after a fashion and because his front paws grew so strong, he was able to climb by pulling himself up. The vet didn't think he would live long but in fact we had Maxie for seven lovely years. A more loving and happy cat you couldn't wish for and I miss him very much.

Phyllis Choppen, Essex

Top tip

Normally, buying clothes out of season is the best way to bag a bargain, so flip-flops in January and winter woollies in August. But when it comes to getting the grandchildren kitted out in their new school uniform, now is generally the best time to buy as shops fight it out to have the best prices for the back-to-school period.

Animal magic

If you've had a sleepless night, spare a thought for the humble ant. The tiny insects don't ever get a proper night's kip - instead they take eight-minute naps twice a day.

Brain teaser

Two letters have already been placed in this grid. Now enter the other 18 given letters to form a rectangle of words, four reading across and five reading down. Each of the letters must take its place in the column or row against which it appears. So the letter T may only appear in the first column, and the letter M only in the top row.

	T	U	I	C	C	
M						S
E			R			A
G				E		D
E						D
	E	G	N	I	S	

My perfect pet

NAME: **Belle**
AGE: **5**
OWNER: **Julie Barker**
PET LIKES: **Cuddles, long walks on the beach and being the centre of attention**
PET HATES: **The hoover, being groomed and the word 'no'**
HUMAN TRAITS: **Sleeping in mum's bed and watching TV**

Recipe of the week

PEANUT BUTTER CHOCOLATE ICE CREAM

Vegan

Serves: 6-8
Preparation time: 15 mins
Freezing time: 2 hrs

4 ripe bananas, peeled, chopped and frozen
200ml (7floz) almond milk
3 tbsp crunchy peanut butter
Plus 2 tbsp for the ripples
60g (2½oz) dark vegan chocolate, chopped fine

1 Put all of the frozen bananas, the almond milk and 3 tbsp of peanut butter into a blender and whizz everything together until the consistency is smooth. This will take a while so keep scraping down the sides and separate any banana chunks that have become frozen together as you go.

2 Once the mix is smooth, remove the blender blade and stir in the chopped chocolate. Tip the ice cream into a freezer container or an old ice cream container. Take the rest of the peanut butter and with a spoon or a fork, dot and swirl in the remaining peanut butter as you go. Cover with a lid or with some cling film and freeze until the ice cream has set. This can take up to 2 hrs depending on your freezer. Remove from the freezer 10 mins before serving. Serve on its own, or with some chopped apple on the side.

Credit: www.meridianfoods.co.uk

4 MONDAY

5 TUESDAY

6 WEDNESDAY

7 THURSDAY

8 FRIDAY

9 SATURDAY

10 SUNDAY

My car crash wedding

Our wedding day was September 11, 1971 and everything was going to plan until the cars were due. One got lost trying to find my aunty's house, then the driver of the bridesmaids' car, which also carried my mum, got his finger trapped in the door and had to go to A&E! So my dad got his car out to run them to church and scraped it badly backing out in a rush while still wearing his reading glasses! Almost an hour later the car turned up for me and Dad and by the time we got to church we were facing a not very happy vicar who wanted to go to the Bolton Wanderers home match which had a late kick-off. (We had arranged our wedding around this just for him.)

That wasn't the end of problems with the cars. The one taking us to the airport broke down en-route. We had to leave it, covered in Just Married messages and with tin cans on the back, outside someone's house. And once again we had to pile into my dad's car. Late, by this time, we dashed through the check-in at Manchester airport while our family and friends went up on the roof – in those less security-conscious days you could still do this – to wave us both off. What we didn't know at the time, was that even our plane was jinxed. Apparently, it took almost the full length of the runway to take off. Fortunately, it made it. They say that accidents come in threes and on my wedding day they certainly did.

Barbara Nuttall, Bolton

Top tip

There's nothing worse than realising too late that you've been charged full price for discount goods. To make it easier both for the cashier to spot the deals and for you to check your receipt, place all the reduced items at the front of the conveyor belt.

Animal magic

Are you a fan of figs? If not, you probably wouldn't last long in the jungle. It turns out that a whopping 70 per cent of rainforest animals and birds rely on the little purple fruit to survive.

Brain teaser

Insert letters into the grid to form six words reading across. When you have finished, the name of a celebrity will be spelt out reading down the blue squares.

I	U	A		A
T	I	P		D
C	N	A		Y
C	I	N		Z
B	M	B		O
I	M	U		E

My perfect pet

NAME: **Poppy**
AGE: **9 weeks**
OWNER: **Brenda Johnson**
PET LIKES: **Digging in the garden and rearranging the plants, bird watching – especially pigeons**
PET HATES: **Water and the vacuum cleaner**
HUMAN TRAITS: **Loves walks on the beach and lots of puddles**

Recipe of the week

ITALIAN SAUSAGES

Serves: 4
Preparation time: 10 mins
Cooking time: 15 mins

3 tbsp olive oil, for frying
1 red onion, peeled and finely chopped
1 garlic clove, peeled and finely chopped
1 tbsp fresh rosemary leaves, finely chopped
400g (14oz) can/packet cooked puy or green lentils
400g (14oz) can plum tomatoes
3 tbsp red wine vinegar
8 Italian sausages or any good quality spicy sausage
Extra virgin olive oil, for drizzling

1 Heat 2 tbsp of olive oil in a large frying pan and add the onion and garlic to the pan. Cook for 5 mins over a medium heat, stirring occasionally. Add the rosemary, stir in and cook for a further 1 min.

2 Add the lentils, tomatoes and vinegar and bring the mixture to the boil. Simmer for 10 mins. Season everything with salt and fresh black pepper. Meanwhile, heat the remaining oil in a large frying pan. Add the sausages and cook everything for 10 mins over a medium heat, turning occasionally to brown on each side.

3 To serve, pour the lentils into a large serving dish and top with the sausages.

4 Drizzle with a little extra virgin olive oil.
Credit: www.cirio1856.co.uk

11 MONDAY

12 TUESDAY

13 WEDNESDAY

14 THURSDAY

15 FRIDAY

16 SATURDAY

17 SUNDAY

Being a brave girl

Believe it or not, my stay in hospital was one of the happiest times of my life. It happened after a neighbour had lost her front-door key in her garden. Although it was raining, we all went to help her find it. I got soaking wet and caught a cold which turned into double pneumonia.

My mum called an ambulance. I remember the children in the street looking at me as I was carried out on a stretcher and taken to Harold Wood hospital. I was very scared and didn't know what to expect. That night I felt so alone as I was only seven and it was the first time I'd been away from my family. My eyes welled up with tears.

Two nurses, immaculate in their starched aprons and caps, came in to give me the first of many injections. "Poor little mite," one of them said. I was brave and never cried.

There was great camaraderie on the children's ward. George, the boy in the next bed, gave me a bundle of Beano and Dandy comics. My best friend, Miriam, had had her appendix taken out. One little girl had broken her arm. We helped each other to get washed and dressed. One day, a nurse told us to put coats on over our nightclothes and took us out for a nature walk which we greatly enjoyed.

All in all, I loved being there. No school, just playing with other children. Admittedly, I didn't like the food very much, but I loved the jelly and ice-cream we had every day.

Linda Mandis, Dagenham

Top tip

Go clothes shopping during the week when the shops are emptier and it's easier for you to try things on calmly. The less stressed you are, the more likely you will make a good decision. Remember, shops tend to arrange clothes by colour and looks, rather than categories such as jeans and tops, apart from when it's sales time. If you spot a shop sorted into types of garments, a sale may be imminent... so wait before you buy.

Animal magic

There may be more than a few differences between our necks and those of giraffes, but when it comes to bones, we've got lots in common. Amazingly they have only seven neck vertebrae – just like us.

Brain teaser

Enter the pairs of letters from the list below into the circles, so that each line running through the central circle produces a six-letter word.

AU
AX
BA
ER
GE
IE
LE
ME
NT
ON
OR
SY
WA

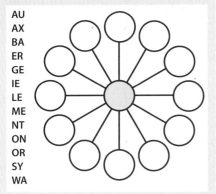

My perfect pet

NAME: **Bella**
AGE: **4**
OWNER: **Debbie Dexter**
PET LIKES: **Mum's electric blanket**
PET HATES: **Going for a walk, loud noises and mum making a fuss of other dogs**
HUMAN TRAITS: **Going to sleep in mum's bed**

Recipe of the week

HONEY-BAKED FIGS

Serves: 2
Preparation time: 2 mins
Cooking time: 5-10 mins

6 figs
4 tsp acacia honey
1 tbsp light olive oil
Small bunch fresh mint

1 Make a shallow cross cut in the top of each fig then place into a snug-fitting shallow ovenproof dish, making sure there is space between each fig. Drizzle over the honey and olive oil into the top cuts of each figs then bake them in a preheated oven at 180°C/350°F/Gas Mark 4 for 5-10 mins.

2 Take them out the oven and check after 5 mins of cooking. If the fruits are ripe they will be warm and ready, if the fruits are a little under-ripe they will take 3-5 mins more.

3 Spoon the honey juices from the base of the dish over the figs then sprinkle the figs with torn mint leaves. You can serve hot or cold. Try serving the figs warm for breakfast with a spoonful of Greek yogurt and a drizzle of honey. Or you could serve them up as part of a meze selection along with a selection of cheese, cold ham, salad and warm bread.
Credit: Rowse Honey

18 MONDAY

19 TUESDAY

20 WEDNESDAY

21 THURSDAY

22 FRIDAY

23 SATURDAY

24 SUNDAY

A different world

I was about seven years old in 1958 and admitted to hospital with chronic osteomyelitis of the right leg. Without going into lots of gory details, lets just say my treatment involved an operation, which was successful up to a point, but I spent the next seven years going backwards and forwards for the same thing without any cure and spent quite a lot of time either on crutches or in a wheelchair.

I remember the children's ward being run by a very fierce sister whose word was strictly the law for staff and children alike! We had visiting times from 2-4pm each afternoon and were never, ever allowed visitors at other times of the day and nobody must sit on the bed. It was strictly two visitors only. Our beds had to be clear of toys, colouring books or whatever our parents had brought in for us to pass the time and we had our hair combed and bed straightened up. I remember the excitement building when the big clock at the end of the ward showed almost 2pm. On several occasions I was sent into the countryside (we lived in Norwich) for convalescence and then it was worse. My parents didn't have a car and bus services were few and far between so I recall once spending two weeks virtually on my own, as Mum and Dad could only manage a couple of visits and the few other children on the ward were allowed outside in the gardens but I was confined to bed. How unthinkable that would be now – and rightly so.
Glynis Anderson, Norfolk

Drive down your car insurance by not automatically renewing your cover. Instead shop around for the best deal - sadly, loyalty doesn't always pay. If you're considered a fairly high-risk driver, consider adding an extra driver to your policy to bring down the price. This second driver should be a relative or friend who would reasonably (and safely) drive your car.

Animal magic

While we always thought elephants had a raw deal, with pregnancies lasting two years, it turns out that shark pregnancies take the biscuit - lasting four years each time.

Brain teaser

Simply shade in one letter in each box of this grid to form a crossword. Proper nouns are not allowed.

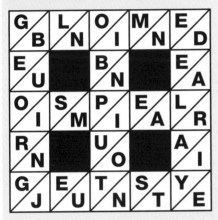

My perfect pet

NAME: **Mirren**
AGE: **1 month**
OWNER: **Lesley Waters**
PET LIKES: **Hay. Following her mum**
PET HATES: **Being separated from her mum and sister. Having her fur ruffled.**
HUMAN TRAITS: **Squabbling with her sister and eating all of the food in the hutch!**

Recipe of the week

NO-BAKE CHOCOLATE CAKE

Serves: 6-8
Preparation time: 20-30 mins

350g (12oz) coconut oil
85g (3oz) cocoa
200g (7oz) icing sugar, plus a little extra for dusting
3 eggs
A few Amaretti biscuits, for decoration
200-250g (7oz-9oz) plain biscuits

1 On a low heat melt the coconut oil and then leave to cool to room temperature. Line a bowl with cling film. Whisk the eggs with a fork until combined.

2 Now mix the cocoa and icing sugar together. Once the oil is cool, mix into the cocoa/icing sugar. Add the eggs and mix with a spatula until you have a smooth cream.

3 Assemble your cake, starting with a thin layer of chocolate cream and then adding the first biscuit. Now add the next layer of cream and the next layer of biscuits. Repeat until you're out of cream. The final layer should be cream.

4 Leave to cool for 2 hrs before transferring to your fridge (putting the cake in the fridge too quickly can result in a grey-ish look). After 1 hr in the fridge the cake should be hardened. Remove from bowl and decorate with the amaretti biscuits and sprinkle with icing sugar.
Credit: Recipe from Carole Poirot at www.ao.com/life

25 MONDAY

26 TUESDAY

27 WEDNESDAY

28 THURSDAY

29 FRIDAY

30 SATURDAY

1 SUNDAY

Through a frosted window

It was 1943 and I was five years old and all I knew was that my mummy had been taken away from me. In fact my mum was in hospital with diphtheria and after two weeks I was taken in with the same thing. I remember going in the ambulance and having to stay in bed for what seemed ages (probably a few days). There was a fire at one end of the ward. Once we were allowed out of bed, we girls were dressed in green-and-white checked dresses with knickers to match, black patent shoes and white socks. One day, a nurse told me that Daddy was coming to see me. She stood me on a chair in front of a window.

At the time I thought it was dirty but, of course, it was frosted. It meant I could see a blurred shape, but not Daddy. Of course there were tears, followed by kind words and a hug from the nurse. The next thing I remember was the nurse giving me a paper bag and telling me what a lucky girl I was and I must not tell anyone. Inside were white and pink fondant sweets. I sat on that chair and ate every one of those sweets! My reward was a slap on the legs and being told what a greedy girl I was. That nurse wasn't so nice after all.

Then one day I was standing looking down a long corridor and a nurse was saying: "Go on - look Mummy and Daddy are waiting for you." Sure enough there were Mum, Dad and my big sister. I can still remember the feeling I got when I saw them.
Maureen Macklin, Hull

Top tip

Get your home ready for winter by bleeding the radiators - they'll be much more efficient (meaning a lower energy bill) once hot water can flow through every part of the radiator. While you're at it, clear your gutters of any leaves and debris that could cause a costly blockage or leak later down the line.

Animal magic

While you might think the clue was in their name, it turns out that scientists aren't sure how to catagorise red pandas. While they may be related to giant pandas, there's a chance that they are closer to skunks or even walruses!

Brain teaser

Fill the blank squares in this grid with digits so that each row, each column and each of the 3 x 3 blocks contains all the digits 1 to 9 once and once only.

	1			6		4		2
8			9		3			
							1	
	9	7		3			4	
4								6
		8		2		3	5	
	8							
			2		6			1
9		5		8			3	

My perfect pet

NAME: **Marley**
AGE: **2**
OWNER: **Jodie and Natasha Goodchild-Gwyther**
PET LIKES: **Belly rubs, chicken and playing with her tennis ball**
PET HATES: **The hoover**
HUMAN TRAITS: **Watching the TV while laying on her back with her legs in the air**

Recipe of the week

APPLE AND ALMOND PIE

Serves: 2
Preparation: 15 mins
Cooking: 30 mins

7 apples
340g (12oz) plain flour
225g (8oz) butter
4 tbsp caster sugar
1 yolk
250ml (9floz) elderflower cordial
100ml (3½oz) water
1 finely grated zest of lemon
25g (1oz) ground almonds
115g (4oz) white marzipan
Flaked almonds
Icing sugar for dusting

1 Put the flour and butter into a processor and whiz until the mixture resembles breadcrumbs. Add the sugar and blend. Now add the yolk and mix again until your pastry comes together into a ball. Chill for 45 mins.

2 Quarter and slice the apples. Put them into a saucepan with the cordial and water, and simmer until tender. Strain off half the liquid into a bowl and discard the rest. Stir in the zest, pour the liquid over the apples and cool. Preheat the oven to 190°C/375°F/Gas Mark 5.

3 Roll out ⅔ of the pastry and line a pie dish. Sprinkle the almonds on the bottom. Break the marzipan into chunks. Spoon the apples into the case, scattering the marzipan over. Form a lattice and cook for 30 mins. About 8 mins before the end, scatter flaked almonds on top. Dust the pie with icing sugar.
Credit: Pink Lady®

2 MONDAY

_____

_____

_____

3 TUESDAY

_____

_____

_____

4 WEDNESDAY

_____

_____

_____

5 THURSDAY

_____

_____

_____

6 FRIDAY

_____

_____

_____

7 SATURDAY

_____

_____

_____

8 SUNDAY

_____

_____

_____

Blast from the past

My deep purple wedding

John and I got married on October 9, 1971 in St James' church, Edgware in Middlesex. I wanted a dress I could wear afterwards and so had it made in a deep purple velvet. Maxi dresses were all the rage then so it was easy to choose one. I never thought of myself as being different but looking at the photos now I suppose I was as I also didn't have a veil or headdress, just flowers in my hair.

My bridesmaid was my sister Anne and I didn't really want anyone else. She wore a dress of mine I already had - it seemed to match mine so there didn't seem any point spending unnecessary money - I had only worn it once before and that was to a staff ball at Buckingham Palace - I knew one of the footmen and he invited me!

I was married by my lovely dad - the Reverend Philip Schofield. He did the same for my sister and I often wonder now whether he ever regretted that this meant that he gave neither of his daughters away - although he never said anything. It is such a proud task for a father to perform. I was given away by my lovely favourite Uncle Rol who had travelled up from South Wales.

He wasn't a well man and I had to support him walking up the aisle. My brother Phil was my chauffeur and just before the end of the service he slipped out, went home, and as John and I walked up the aisle my beloved pet dog Mandy came running down the aisle to greet us and join in the celebration!
Gwyn Grocott, Cheshire

Top tip

It's easy to stuff our receipts in our bags without so much as a glance at them. But taking time to read your receipts could reap big savings. Many retailers put money off your next shop or a discount code at the bottom of your receipt to entice you back again. So make sure to store these somewhere safe and take them along with you next time you shop.

Animal magic

We're not recommending you test this out, but if a snail's eye is cut off the slimy creature can just regrow another one. It saves a trip to Specsavers.

Brain teaser

The card on the left contains 21 words. See if you can find 10 pairs, taken from either column, and write your answers in the card on the right. When you have finished, you will discover one word which won't fit with any of the others. Which one is it?

21	Mount	21	21
Lauderdale	Lake		
Long	Springs		
Corpus	Little		
Green	Placid		
Cod	Sioux		
Beverly	Island		
Fort	Christi		
Colorado	Cape		
Falls	Pleasant		
Rock	Hills		

My perfect pet

NAME: **Molly**
AGE: **10**
OWNER: **Christine Wootton**
PET LIKES: **Sunbathing on the dustbin outside and sitting on all freshly ironed piles of clothes**
PET HATES: **The dustbin men, bin liners and the vacuum cleaner**
HUMAN TRAITS: **She gets very cross when she's hungry**

Recipe of the week

CHOCOLATE OVERNIGHT OATS

Serves: 2
Preparation: 5 mins
Cooking: none required

For the oats:
100g (3½oz) porridge oats
250ml (9floz) almond milk/oat milk/cow's milk
1 ripe banana, peeled and mashed to a pulpy mush
1 tbsp cocoa powder
1 tbsp clear honey
For the topping:
2 tbsp toasted, flaked almonds or chopped almonds
Fresh blueberries, raspberries, strawberries
2 squares dark chocolate, roughly chopped

1 Mix the oats, your chosen milk, mashed banana, cocoa powder along with the clear honey together in a bowl. Stir the oat mixture until everything is well combined and leave in the bowl. Or divide between two jam jars, screw the lids on your jars tightly and give them a good shake to thoroughly mix everything together. Place the mixture in the fridge overnight so the oats soak up all the ingredients. Take out of the fridge and give everything a good stir.

2 To serve, top with flaked and toasted almonds, all of the fresh berries and a few chunks of dark chocolate that have been roughly chopped. Eat straight away.
Credit: Rowse Honey

9 **MONDAY**

10 **TUESDAY**

11 **WEDNESDAY**

12 **THURSDAY**

13 **FRIDAY**

14 **SATURDAY**

15 **SUNDAY**

Colonial typing memories

In 1948, when I was 17, I saw an advertisement in the paper. The Civil Service wanted typists and they were willing to train applicants. I applied and passed the entrance exam and started at the typing school, just behind the Dominion Theatre in Tottenham Court Road, London. There were two classes and we all learned to the rhythm of Victor Sylvester.

How I remember plodding along to 'I Wonder Who's Kissing Her Now?' on my manual Underwood! Then in the next class it would be quicksteps because of the increased speed. After our training, we were allocated to different Government departments. Mine was the Colonial Office in Victoria Street, along from the Army and Navy stores. Those were the days when Britain still had colonies such as Tanganyika, Nyasaland and Rhodesia. Our typing pool was attached to the welfare department and dealt with colonial students who came over to study at our universities. One time, I had to write a report of several pages - one copy, plus four carbons.

Throughout, the word itinerary cropped up and because of our lazy way of speaking, I typed itinary. Can you imagine going through all those carbons and squeezing in those extra 'er's. It would have been quicker to retype the whole thing. I was then transferred to the Private Office. There I used a typewriter with bulletin type which meant the letters were about four times as large. This was because James Griffiths, who was Secretary of State for the Colonies then, didn't like to wear his spectacles in the House of Commons.
June Sandison, Middx

Top tip

When your tub of body scrub is starting to run out, rather than buying another one, just make it last longer. Top it up with some brown sugar or Epsom salts and a little olive or coconut oil. These kitchen cupboard staples have skin-soothing properties and will save you a packet on your beauty regime.

Animal magic

If bees were paid the minimum wage for their hard work, a single jar of honey would cost somewhere around £131,402 - so make the most of your morning toast!

Brain teaser

To conquer this one, fill in the blank spaces of this crossword with all 26 letters of the alphabet. Keep track of your progress by crossing off the letters below as you go.

ABCDEFGHIJKLMNOPQRSTUVWXYZ

My perfect pet

NAMES: **Mr Darcy and Oscar**
AGE: **8**
OWNER: **Pat and Roger Wells**
PET LIKES: **Sitting on the windowsill barking at passers by**
PET HATES: **Cats, squirrels and wormers**
HUMAN TRAITS: **Likes sleeping on the bed and cleaning the kitchen floor of crumbs**

Recipe of the week

HONEYED PUMPKIN PIES

Serves: 4
Preparation time: 20 mins
Cooking time: 20-25 mins

For the pastry:
225g (8oz) plain flour
50g (2oz) caster sugar
100g (4oz) butter, diced
2 egg yolks
2-3 teaspoons cold water
For the filling:
450g (1lb) deseeded pumpkin, peeled, diced
75g (3oz) Rowse Acacia honey
75g (3oz) light muscovado sugar
3 eggs
1 tsp ground ginger
½ tsp ground mixed spice

1 Add the flour and sugar to a bowl, add the butter and rub in. Mix in the egg yolks and enough water to form to a dough. Chill for 15 mins.

2 Steam the pumpkin for 10-15 mins until tender. Drain and cool then mash or purée in a liquidiser or food processor. Add the remaining filling ingredients and mix again.

3 Roll the pastry and cut out 12×10 cm (4in) circles. Press the pastry circles into a 12-hole muffin tin. Reserve the trimmings.

4 Pour the pumpkin filling into the cases. Roll the pastry trimmings, cut into strips, brush lightly with milk and arrange as a lattice over the top of the tarts, sticking with milk.

5 Sprinkle with caster sugar and bake for 180°C/350°F/Gas Mark 4 for 20-25 mins. Leave to cool. Lift out of the tin. Serve warm or cold.
Credit: Rowse Honey

16 MONDAY

17 TUESDAY

18 WEDNESDAY

19 THURSDAY

20 FRIDAY

21 SATURDAY

22 SUNDAY

Blast from the past

Our labour of love

Our first house had five bedrooms, three gardens (one of them walled), no heating, an outside privy, no bathroom and a single tap in the scullery as our only source of water. In 1960, newly returned from a service posting abroad, we were too young for married quarters, so decided to buy. Being short of money, meant we had to go for the cheaper end of the market and this 16th century farmhouse was all we could afford. We had no furniture, but the salerooms were a wonderful source of everything we needed. We bought a 'put-u-up' – an early type of sofa-bed; various tables and chairs, a Burco boiler, washtub and mangle and a large piece of carpeting, somewhat worn, which came from a stately home – very posh! In the six years we lived there we picked the brains of the local craftsmen and did most of the installation of bathroom and kitchen units ourselves.

My husband filled the intervals between flying aeroplanes with plumbing, electrical wiring and plastering, with me as builder's mate. When I was expecting twins I could be found happily mixing cement and became a dab hand at interior decorating and curtain-making. We meant to make this our home for ever, but one day a couple knocked on the door and said they wanted to buy our house. By now, we had four children and were still short of money. Their offer was beyond generous. Also the question of regular service postings caused problems. So common sense made up our minds for us. Our memories of that wonderful house are treasured by the whole family.
Pat Evans, Haverfordwest

Top tip

Supermarkets tend to change their deals and release new bargain offers mid-week. So shopping on a Wednesday or Thursday could be the key to saving yourself a packet at the check-out. And it's the same if you shop online as new deals typically become available on websites in the middle of the week too.

Animal magic

Alarmingly, we share an enormous 70 per cent of our DNA with that of a slug, and a massive 98.4 per cent with that of a chimp.

Brain teaser

Write each answer in a clockwise direction around its clue number in the grid. When you have finished, the central yellow hexagons will reveal the name of a place in Europe

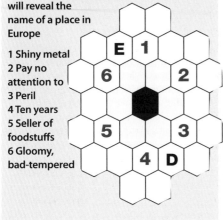

1 Shiny metal
2 Pay no attention to
3 Peril
4 Ten years
5 Seller of foodstuffs
6 Gloomy, bad-tempered

My perfect pet

NAME: **Blackberry**
AGE: **3**
OWNER: **Rosemary Parker**
PET LIKES: **Carrots. Playing with his best friend – the dog**
PET HATES: **Other rabbits making his hutch a mess. The rain. Cats coming into the pen.**
HUMAN TRAITS: **Likes keeping his hutch tidy**

Recipe of the week

POT-ROASTED CHICKEN

Serves: 4
Preparation time: 10 mins
Cooking time: 1 hr 20 mins

1.5kg chicken
1 lemon, quartered
3 tbsp olive oil
2 onions, finely chopped
2 large carrots, finely chopped
2 sticks celery, finely chopped
2 bay leaves, fresh or dried
2 sprigs rosemary
2 cloves garlic, crushed
1 tbsp of plain flour
275ml (½pint) dry cider
275ml (½pint) chicken stock
2 large apples, cored and cut into wedges
3 tbsp crème fraîche
1 tbsp flat leaf parsley, chopped

1 Preheat the oven to 200°C/400°F/Gas Mark 6. Stuff the chicken with the lemon. Drizzle over 1 tbsp of oil and season. Roast for 30 mins.

2 Add the rest of the oil to a casserole dish. Sweat the onion, carrot and celery with the bay leaves and rosemary.

3 Once the onion and carrot are soft, add the garlic and fry for 1 min before stirring through the flour. Pour in the cider, stock and season.

4 Remove the chicken from the oven and reduce the heat. Lay the chicken on top of the vegetables. Cover and cook for 1 hr then add the apple. Return to the oven, uncovered, and cook for 20 mins. Stir through the crème fraîche and parsley.
Credit: Pink Lady®

23 MONDAY

24 TUESDAY

25 WEDNESDAY

26 THURSDAY

27 FRIDAY

28 SATURDAY

29 SUNDAY

Those dreaded duplicators!

I was a junior secretary and the thing which I hated was the Gestetner Ink Duplicator - there were no photocopiers, or electric typewriters, in the Sixties for us. It was necessary to create a template, this being typed on a sort of thin wax sheet, which had a carbon sheet attached underneath it, both sheets being then attached to a thin card. The keys on the typewriter punctured the wax and at the same time created the carbon copy. If you made an error, the only way to correct it was to paint a thin layer of bright pink correcting fluid on to the error, wait for it to dry then type over the top of it - but with the three layers of papers it often meant that the underneath ones moved so the carbon copy was misplaced. To print the finished document off, it had to be attached to a large drum on the Gestetner machine, very carefully pressed flat all round the drum, making certain there were no creases, and then the ink lever was pressed and the electricity set in motion to print off the copies - it was very messy!

Once the printing was done, you then had to remove the, by now, very inky template and lay it flat to dry, as you had to keep it in case it was needed again in the future. I wonder how today's personal assistants would manage. If, as so often happened, you got ink on your clothes, the only way to remove it was to use amyl acetate, which smelt heavily of pear drops.

Hazel Cole, Bucks

Top tip

Prepare for the chilly winter ahead by buying your boiler a new jacket. Adding another layer to your hot water cylinder prevents too much heat escaping and could save you a significant amount on your energy bill. These are easy to fit by yourself and should cost no more than £10 from your local DIY store. You'll need a jacket that's at least 75mm thick to do the job efficiently.

Animal magic

Java sparrows have specific tastes when it comes to classical music. The little birds appear to prefer the works of Bach and Vivaldi, as they listen longer to music by these composers.

Brain teaser

From the letters of the words given below, form six five-letters words to fit the grid. Three letters have been inserted already and here is a clue to the first word reading across:
Remove dirt

CAVE   EXACT   RARE   ROLL   VENT

	■	X	■	
V	■		■	V

My perfect pet

NAME: **Jezebel**
AGE: **22 weeks**
OWNER: **Benn Powell**
PET LIKES: **Chasing balls in the park. Any ball will do - not just her own!**
PET HATES: **Going home from the park on a sunny day**
HUMAN TRAITS: **She likes to drink tea out of a cup**

Recipe of the week

LAMB PUMPKIN PIES

Serves: 6
Preparation time: 25 mins
Cooking time: 30 mins

450g (1lb) cubed Welsh lamb shoulder
1 onion, roughly chopped
1 tsp ground cumin
½ small pumpkin or butternut squash, peeled and cubed
300ml (½pt) lamb stock
25g (1oz) sultanas
25g (1oz) pine nuts
2 sprigs fresh rosemary
500g (17½oz) butter puff pastry
1 egg and splash milk mixed together for glazing

1 Heat oil, add the onion and brown. Add the cubed lamb and brown, then add in the cumin and stir.

2 Add the pumpkin or squash, stock, sultanas, pine nuts and season. Drop in a sprig of rosemary, before putting on the lid. Simmer for 30 mins.

3 Remove from the heat and ladle into a family-sized pie dish or four individual pie dishes. Reserve a little juice for gravy.

4 Remove the pastry from the packaging and press a small sprig of rosemary into it. Take a rolling pin and roll out the pastry to fit the pie dish. Place the pastry on the dish, brush with egg and milk glaze and place in an oven at 200°C/400°F/Gas Mark 6 for 25 mins until the pastry has risen and become golden.

Credit: www.eatwelshlambandwelshbeef.com

30 MONDAY

31 TUESDAY

1 WEDNESDAY

2 THURSDAY

3 FRIDAY

4 SATURDAY

5 SUNDAY

We were £10 poms

We emigrated to Australia in the early Seventies as part of the mass immigration paid for by the Australian government. We paid £10 (£10 poms) for our passage on the SS Australis bound for Sydney from Southampton. We were my husband John and our three children Paul, nine, Kim, seven and Maria, five. My husband had always dreamed of living down under.

Eventually, we set off to Brisbane from Sydney, along the Pacific Highway in a bright orange and cream camper van. We took three weeks and camped out each night under the stars. There were all kinds of wildlife, from kookaburras to kangaroos, exotic cockatoos to woolly wombats. We had to look out for snakes and spiders with names such as redback and funnel-web which could give you a nasty bite or render you unconscious if you were too far away from medical assistance. Christmas beetles were huge fat things that developed wings and flew blind in December. They invaded open doors and windows, banging into walls and furniture until, exhausted, they dropped at your feet. Mosquitos buzzed and bit every exposed part of my anatomy, seeming to like my sweet sweat. No one else in the family attracted them like I did.

You may not believe it but I enjoyed every moment of that three-week adventure. The family settled just outside Brisbane in a lovely house. We stayed in Australia three years and achieved so much. Then my husband was seriously injured at work and we took the decision to return to England. My husband died seven years later from a sudden heart attack. But I had the consolation of knowing that I had helped him achieve his dream.
Christine McCherry, Blackpool

Top tip

Meat is one of the priciest foodstuffs we buy, but being more adventurous in the cuts of meat you eat could save you a fortune. For stews or casseroles, choose stewing brisket, skirt or shin of beef. For pork, try spare ribs or belly, and go for the shoulder, scrag or middle neck of lamb. And for a roast chicken, use the whole bird including the bones for stock, which can be frozen for later.

Animal magic

Catnaps must be good for the brain, as it turns out our feline friends have better memories than dogs or monkeys. They can recall events for up to 16 hours, compared with a dog's five-minute memory.

Brain teaser

Fill the blank squares in this grid with digits so that each row, each column and each of the 3 x 3 blocks contains all the digits 1 to 9 once and once only.

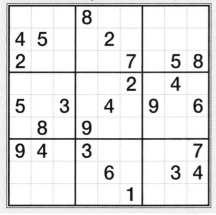

My perfect pet

NAME: **Delilah**
AGE: **6**
OWNER: **Stacey Carter**
PET LIKES: **Walks, doing obedience and eating gravy bones**
PET HATES: **Balloons, having her teeth brushed and baths**
HUMAN TRAITS: **Has a sweet tooth and enjoys human food too much! She also snores horrendously at night.**

Recipe of the week

CHOCOLATE BATS

Serves: 9
Preparation time: 1 hr
Cooking time: 5 mins

125g (4½oz) cake crumbs
25g of cocoa powder
40g (1½oz) icing sugar
50g (2oz) butter
1 tsp peppermint extract
150g (5oz) dark chocolate
To decorate:
75g (3oz) dark chocolate
Dr. Oetker White Icing
Dr. Oetker Bright Writing Icing (Red)

1 Place the cake crumbs in a bowl and sift in the cocoa and icing sugar. Mix in the melted butter and peppermint. Form into 9 balls and place on a lined plate. Cover and chill until firm.

2 Melt the dark chocolate. Using a bat-shaped template, trace 9 sets of wings on a sheet of baking parchment. Put the parchment on a large board.

3 Spoon ⅓ of the melted chocolate into a piping bag without a nozzle. Snip a little of the bag away at the end and pipe around each wing shape to give an outline in melted chocolate. Leave for a few mins to set, then fill in the centres with melted chocolate. Leave to cool.

4 Place a small sheet of baking parchment on another board and pipe the outline of 9 pairs of ears. Once set, fill in the centre with melted chocolate.

5 Coat the chilled cake balls with the 75g (3oz) of melted chocolate. Peel off a pair of wings and ears and press into the sides and top of each ball. Cool for 15 mins.

6 Pipe on the whites of the eyes and a mouth. Re-melt any leftover chocolate, and pipe or brush on for eye balls and noses. Leave to set.
Credit: Dr. Oetker

6 **MONDAY**

7 **TUESDAY**

8 **WEDNESDAY**

9 **THURSDAY**

10 **FRIDAY**

11 **SATURDAY**

12 **SUNDAY**

The games we played

I was a secretary for many years. The computers we have today make work a lot easier. Indeed they make the old typewriters, which I worked on, seem so outdated. But looking back, there were some things you could do with a typewriter which no computer can do.

For instance... One office I was in had eight secretaries sitting together and the young juniors would often come and ask if there was any typing they could do for us. If we had handwritten letters or labels needing typing we would let them do this. A couple of these girls were always joking around, so after they had gone we would remove the ribbon from the typewriter and call them back.

The girl would sit down, put paper in the typewriter and start to type, but obviously nothing appeared on the paper. She would call us over and say something was wrong and we said it had to be her as it was working prior to her taking over. So she tried again. But we couldn't keep a straight face for long and eventually told her what we had done.

Another thing we did was loosen the screws on the carriage so when they came to do a carriage return the carriage flew off the typewriter and on to the desk. Typewriters were sturdy so no damage was done. Obviously you could only do this once, but we all had a laugh - happy days!

June Hawkridge, Nottingham

Top tip

Looking for a winter getaway? Save on skiing breaks by choosing less well-known ski resorts as they will often be cheaper. Eastern Europe has some amazing facilities at low prices, so think Slovenia, Serbia, Poland and Bulgaria and closer to home Andorra. Skiers can also pre-book their equipment with most travel agents or tour operators so there are no surprise costs when they get there.

Animal magic

While you might not fancy running into a lion, it's not the King of the Jungle who causes the most human deaths. In fact, it's hippos - who kill more people in Africa than lions, elephants, leopards, buffalo, and rhinos combined.

Brain teaser

Fit the five-letter words listed below into the pentagons, in a clockwise direction. Where the pentagons join, the letters in the facing segments must be the same. We've placed three letters in the grid to get you started.

GRIME
JUDGE
MAUVE
PLEAD
PLUCK
PUPPY
SCOWL
SLING
STICK
STIFF
THROB
TRUST

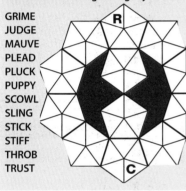

My perfect pet

NAME: **Oscar**
AGE: **3**
OWNER: **Kristine Griffin**
PET LIKES: **Chasing rabbits down holes and food**
PET HATES: **Having a bath**
HUMAN TRAITS: **Sleeping on my owner's bed**

Recipe of the week

CUSTARD TART

Serves: 6
Preparation time: 20 mins
Cooking time: 45 mins

For the pastry:
175g (6oz) plain flour
¼ tsp of salt
65g (2½oz) Trex
2 tsp caster sugar
1 egg yolk
1 tbsp chilled water
For the custard:
2 large eggs
2 egg yolks
40g (1½oz) caster sugar
150ml (¼pt) single cream
300ml (½pt) milk
1 vanilla pod

1 Sift the flour and salt and rub in the Trex. Stir in the sugar. Beat an egg yolk and water together and pour in. Bring the mixture together, then form into a ball. Knead, then chill.

2 Roll out the dough. Lift it into a 20cm (8in) pie plate or flan ring. Chill for 15 mins. Preheat the oven to 200°C/400°F/Gas Mark 6.

3 Line the pastry case and bake blind for 15 mins. Remove the beans. Bake for 5 mins and cool.

4 Reduce the oven to 150°C/300°F/Gas Mark 2. Beat the eggs, egg yolks and sugar together. Heat the cream, milk and vanilla pod to below boiling point, then remove and infuse for 10 mins. Add the seeds from the vanilla pod. Whisk into the egg.

5 Strain into the pastry case, then sprinkle with nutmeg. Bake for 45 mins and cool.
Credit: Trex

13 MONDAY

14 TUESDAY

15 WEDNESDAY

16 THURSDAY

17 FRIDAY

18 SATURDAY

19 SUNDAY

Childhood sweethearts

When the Second World War broke out in 1939 I was a pupil at Clapton Country Secondary School in London. I was evacuated to the market town of Bishop's Stortford in East Hertfordshire and was lucky enough to be billeted with a lovely family. They were named Livings and they had two daughters, Jean and Betty. And I also met a young lad called Cliff... I eventually returned to London a few years later in 1942 and went to work in the heart of the City of London for the Royal Exchange Assurance Company whose offices were opposite the Bank of England in Threadneedle Street. At that time there would always be someone on the roof, watching the skies. When the watcher knew that the dreaded V1 or V2s were approaching he would raise a flag and we all had to descend many flights of stairs into the basement of the building. Sometimes we would be up and down all day without much time at all for actual work.

However, I met many famous people during the course of my work, including Sir Malcolm Campbell, the famous racing driver who broke the land speed record, as I handed them interest on their investments. Cliff and I had stayed in touch and we got married in 1945. As happened to many at that time, he then went off to Kenya, attached to the King's African Rifles and didn't return until 1947. We were quite happy to settle down in Bishop's Stortford and raise our family – two sons, three grandsons and now five great-grandsons and one great-granddaughter. Cliff died in 2015, just five days after we celebrated our 70th wedding anniversary.
Kathleen Barker, Bishop's Stortford

Top tip

If you'd like to lose a few pounds or just get a little fitter, don't wait for the New Year to make a resolution. Gym memberships are usually at their cheapest just after the post-summer slump and before the January rush to get fit begins, so it pays to sign up now.

Brain teaser

The nine-letter answers to the three clues can all be found in the grid below. Start at the first letter and trace the word from letter to adjacent letter in a wiggly line. You may move diagonally, but no square may be visited more than once in each word.

Clues

1 Weaken gradually
2 Magnificence
3 Frantic, without hope

E	A	N	I
T	E	R	M
P	E	D	U
S	L	N	O

My perfect pet

NAME: **Ronnie Bear**
AGE: **8**
OWNER: **Sarah and Fred**
PET LIKES: **Long walks, big hugs, meeting people, rides in the car and watching TV**
PET HATES: **Being indoors**
HUMAN TRAITS: **Watches TV and is in charge of the remote control**

Recipe of the week

CHAI PORRIDGE

Serves: 1
Preparation time: 5 mins
Cooking time: 15 mins

50g (2oz) Flahavan's Irish Porridge Oats
350ml (½pint) semi-skimmed milk
3 juniper berries/spice berries
1 thin slice ginger, peeled and chopped
1 cinnamon stick
¼ tsp nutmeg
Pinch ground clove
Zest of 1 clementine
2 tbsp maple syrup
1 heaped tsp cranberry sauce

1 Add the milk, spices and clementine zest to a small saucepan and gently bring the mixture to the boil over a low heat - this should take around 5 mins.

2 Once boiled, remove the milk from the heat and allow the spices to infuse in the saucepan for 10 mins.

3 Strain the milk and spice mixture through a sieve and pour the porridge mixture into another saucepan.

4 Add the oats and maple syrup to the milk mixture and bring to the boil. Once boiled, simmer the mixture for 4-5 mins until it has a creamy consistency.

5 Top the porridge with a spoonful of your favourite cranberry sauce and a sprinkling of cinnamon and chopped nuts to serve.
Credit: Flahavens Oats

20 MONDAY

21 TUESDAY

22 WEDNESDAY

23 THURSDAY

24 FRIDAY

25 SATURDAY

26 SUNDAY

Beware balance sheets

In the days when all offices were only equipped with manual typewriters, I spent a year working in the typing pool of a large firm of accountants. I remember that the entirety of my first week was spent carefully practising drawing double lines perfectly and sewing up balance sheets. To type balance sheets properly one needed, at most, to be a mathematician, as it involved setting out columns of figures over eighty spaces! It required great concentration and fantastic precision. Nowadays I have watched my son shift blocks of figures wherever needed at the touch of a button on a computer. We had no such magic device.

But, as they say, practice makes perfect and I was selected to go to the top public school, Eton, to type up their balance sheets. I remember that it was May time and I was struck by how beautiful the surroundings were and I remember I could hear the cuckoo calling. Back in those days of reasonably full employment you could pick and choose jobs. So I elected to go and work in the medical world, which held greater interest for me, and left the field of commerce. I happily settled in a medical school and then later on, when I returned to work after my son was born, I got a job at my local hospital. And that was where I remained, very happily, until I retired. After all, if you are interested and content in your work, you do not notice the hard graft.
Irene Clegg, Kent

Top tip

Looking for a fun and thrifty Christmas present? Pay for your loved ones to go to classes to learn a new skill, whether that's cookery, woodwork, knitting or whatever. This is also a great way to help your family save some pennies as they'll be able to make their own things once they've mastered their new craft.

Animal magic

There's no piece of jewellery more precious than a wedding ring, and it turns out that Gentoo penguins have their own equivalent. Male birds 'propose' to their prospective mates by presenting them with a pebble.

Brain teaser

Shade in one letter in each box of this grid to form a crossword. Proper nouns are not allowed.

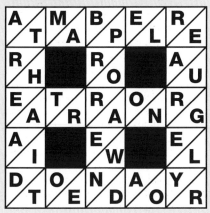

My perfect pet

NAME: **Poppy**
AGE: **2**
OWNER: **Anne Davies**
PET LIKES: **Lounging in the bed all day**
PET HATES: **Other cats in her garden**
HUMAN TRAITS: **Sitting up at the table to eat**

Recipe of the week

VEGETABLE GRATIN

Serves: 4
Preparation time: 10 mins
Cooking time: 25 mins

400g can Cirio Chopped Tomatoes
4 tbsp Filippo Berio Olive Oil
2 red onions, peeled and finely sliced
2 garlic cloves, peeled and finely chopped
2 tsp dried oregano
750g (1½lb) aubergines, cut into 1cm cubes
2 tbsp balsamic vinegar
3 tbsp fresh basil
100g (3½oz) Parmesan cheese, grated
300g (11oz) courgettes, thinly sliced
2x100g balls mozzarella cheese, torn

1 Preheat the oven to 180°C/375°F/ Gas Mark 4. Heat 2 tbsp of olive oil in a frying pan and add the onion, garlic and half of the oregano. Cook over a medium heat for 5 mins.

2 Add the remaining olive oil and turn the heat up. Add the aubergine and cook for 3 mins. Add the chopped tomatoes and vinegar and simmer for 2 mins. Stir in the basil and half of the Parmesan.

3 Spread the mixture on the bottom of a gratin dish. Dot with the mozzarella and top with courgette ribbons. Sprinkle with the remaining Parmesan. Drizzle with olive oil and cook for 15 mins in the oven.
Credit: Cirio Tomatoes

27	MONDAY

28	TUESDAY

29	WEDNESDAY

30	THURSDAY

1	FRIDAY

2	SATURDAY

3	SUNDAY

Blast from the past

Where was Mam?

In 1942, aged four, I became very ill with scarlet fever. This was six years before the NHS, so who paid for my treatment I don't know – but it meant fumigating the house and six weeks in an isolation hospital. I have little recollection of my time in there because I was so poorly, but what bits I do recall were not good. The place was starkly clean and the beds were sectioned off, in pairs, by large glass windows, so that you could see other beds and nurses around you, but were cut off from everybody except the boy in the other bed, who was as scared as I was. So we never spoke to one another.

I remember at one time being walked along a veranda for a bath. The bathroom was white and shiny with a big white bath which the nurse filled with thundering steaming water. The water was very warm and so unlike the Friday night tin-bath in front of the fire I was used to that after she had lifted me in, I didn't know what I was supposed to do. The nurse seemed put out by my hesitation, so I braved the heat and washed myself as best I could.

My lack of visitors was a puzzle. I found out years later that Mam had been walking three miles every day to the Town Hall to read the hospital's bulletin board. I was listed as 'very poorly' for a while and she would cry to herself all the way home. Eventually I was listed as 'poorly, but comfortable', then 'comfortable'. She must have been worried to death, but she knew her place and wouldn't have dreamt of pushing herself in at the hospital.

Jeff Williams, Cheshire

Top tip

It's time to get on your glad rags for those Christmas parties. But rather than paying over the odds for a dress you might only wear once, why not consider renting a dress? Some designer shops and fancy dress stores allow you to rent an outfit for a few days. And if you're online, that-dress.net, girlmeetsdress.com and myredcarpetdress.co.uk are great places to look for glam numbers to hire that cost a fraction of the price you'd pay to buy.

Animal magic

If you ever worry that your dance moves leave much to be desired, you're in good company. The majority of the animal kingdom is bad at boogying – it's only parrots that can dance in time to a beat.

Brain teaser

Enter single-digit numbers into the empty triangles in this grid so that the figures in each hexagon add up to 26. No number can appear twice in the same hexagon and nought cannot be used.

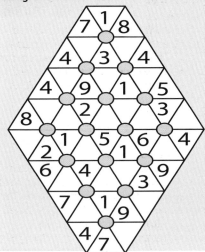

My perfect pet

NAME: **Lucy**
AGE: **14**
OWNER: **Angela Wharrard**
PET LIKES: **Sleeping in her armchair in the sun**
PET HATES: **Cold wet weather**
HUMAN TRAITS: **Likes to talk and sing a lot**

Recipe of the week

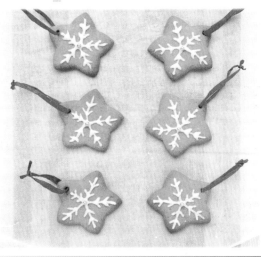

CINNAMON STAR COOKIES

Serves: 10-12
Preparation time: 30 mins
Cooking time: 8-10 mins

45g (1½oz) slightly salted butter
75g (3oz) golden syrup
30g (1oz) caster sugar
125g (4oz) plain flour (plus extra for dusting)
1½ tsp cinnamon
1¼ tsp bicarbonate of soda
75g (3oz) icing sugar
2 tbsp water
1 tsp edible silver balls
1 metre red ribbon or string

1 Put the butter, syrup and sugar in a pan and melt. Put the flour, cinnamon and bicarbonate of soda into a bowl and add the cooled syrup. Mix until combined. Work the mix into a ball and chill for 30 mins.

2 Roll out to 5mm (¼in) thick. Cut out star shapes. Make a hole for the ribbon near the tips. Place the stars on a lined baking tray. Bake for 8 mins until golden brown, then cool.

3 Mix the water and icing together until you have a thick paste. Starting from the centre of a cookie, pipe the icing in lines out to towards each point. Pipe details along each line. Pop a silver ball in the centre of each.

4 Thread an 8-10cm (3in-4in) ribbon through each hole and tie off to finish.

Credit: www.ao.com/life

4 MONDAY

5 TUESDAY

6 WEDNESDAY

7 THURSDAY

8 FRIDAY

9 SATURDAY

10 SUNDAY

My amazing dad

My late father Laddie Peare, was my hero. He was honest, handsome, hardworking, kind, generous and ingenious. He was landlord of the famous coaching inn, the Trouble House Inn in Tetbury. But he originally came from farming stock and this was where his heart lay – so he rented land for keeping livestock and growing crops.

Father knew his flowers, wildlife and the seasons – so he instinctively knew when to sow and when to reap. He rented a field opposite the inn where he kept Highland sheep and he needed to find an easier way of getting water to them than having to hump churns of water across every day. He decided he would pass a hosepipe under the road through a large soak-way pipe. The problem was – how?

From the inn side of the road he pushed the hosepipe as far as he could under the road but, frustratingly, it stopped short. How to grab the other end of it? At that point who should he spy but me – then a school girl. "I've got a job for you girl. I need you to crawl up that pipe and grasp the hosepipe and reverse out with it. Got that?" Of course I replied: "Yep, Dad – no problem." Well it wasn't – until I crawled in. Crawling in wet, slimy, smelly mud, the further I went the darker it got, with my body obliterating the light. I tried and tried, each time scuttling back. My fear grew with every attempt and I had to give up. Somehow my dad succeeded although I can't remember how – but then my dad could do anything! By the way, the parrot in the photo was Dad's cockatoo, Georgie. I now look after him and he is 54.

Janet Peare, Carmarthenshire

Top tip

Christmas is typically a time for indulgence, but that doesn't have to mean the festive season should eat up your bank balance. When planning the Christmas Day feast, try to buy your long-lasting staples now before supermarkets put their prices up. And be sure to plan out your meal in advance and then make a shopping list, so you don't get panicked into buying more than you really need.

Animal magic

If you're accident prone spare a thought for orangutans. Apparently 50 per cent have fractured bones after falling out of trees on a regular basis. Ouch.

Brain teaser

Fill the blank squares in this grid with digits so that each row, each column and each of the 3 x 3 blocks contains all the digits 1 to 9 once and once only.

	5	9		6				
7				3				4
	1						9	
			1			8		
	4		6		5		1	
		9			2			
	7						6	
6				7				2
			3		8	7		

My perfect pet

NAME: **Bertie**
AGE: **3 and a half**
OWNER: **Janette Carter**
PET LIKES: **Apples and other female guinea pigs**
PET HATES: **Being picked up and drinking from bottles – he prefers a dish of water**
HUMAN TRAITS: **Grumpy. Likes a lie in**

Recipe of the week

MINCE PIES

Serves: 12
Preparation time: 15 mins
Cooking time: 25 mins

225g (8oz) plain flour
¼ salt
85g (3¼oz) Trex
1 tbsp of icing sugar
Finely grated zest of 1 orange and 2 tbsp of juice
1 small egg beaten with 1 tbsp of cold water
For the filling:
4 tbsp of mincemeat
50g (2oz) cream cheese

1 Sift the flour and salt into a bowl and rub in the Trex. Stir in the icing sugar, orange zest, orange juice and 2 tbsp of the beaten egg mixture. Mix together until the pastry clings together. Form the dough into a ball and chill for 10 mins.

2 Preheat the oven to 200°C/400°F/Gas Mark 6.

3 Roll out the pastry until 5mm (¼in) thick. Stamp 12 rounds with a 7.5cm (3in) cutter, then 12 rounds with a 6cm (2½in) cutter. Alternatively, use a star-shaped cutter to stamp out the tops.

4 Place the larger rounds of pastry into patty tins and add 1 level tsp of mincemeat, then 1 level tsp of cream cheese. Brush the pastry rims with the egg, place the lids on top, seal, then glaze with beaten egg.

5 Bake for 20-25 mins. Cool then serve with icing sugar.
Credit: Trex

11 MONDAY

12 TUESDAY

13 WEDNESDAY

14 THURSDAY

15 FRIDAY

16 SATURDAY

17 SUNDAY

One of the boys in blue

In November 1960 I left my civilian career as an undertaker to embark on two years national service with the Royal Air Force, one of the last intake to do so.

Two months earlier I had been required to attend a medical examination to establish whether I was fit enough to be called up. As I had been granted deferment to complete a course I was doing at a local college, I had assumed there would be no national service for me - until a brown official envelope with O.H.M.S. printed on it landed on my doormat.

Although a reluctant airman, I soon coped with the initial 12 weeks at RAF Cardington, where I learned to march and fire a 303 rifle. I then completed an intensive course to become a telex operator, achieving a speed of 55 words a minute on a teleprinter.

Eventually I was posted to Church Fenton in Yorkshire and from there to RAF Valley in Anglesey where I worked in the signals section, sending classified and routine messages to various military establishments in the UK and abroad.

As Valley was located some miles from my home in Holyhead I bought an old BSA 125cc motorbike which had a wooden seat for the pillion rider. This enabled me to visit my wife, Betty, and our baby son when I was off duty.

The two years soon passed. Looking back, I believe the training and comradeship proved to be an advantage, building my self-confidence and discipline.
Melvyn Griffiths, Anglesey

Top tip

If you're going all out and buying expensive presents for a loved one this Christmas, make sure you let your insurer know so it's insured. And if you're buying presents online worth between £100 and £30,000, use your credit card. A law in the Consumer Credit Act means that if you use your credit card (not including debit cards) the card company is jointly liable for the full amount of the purchase if it doesn't turn up or is faulty.

Animal magic

If you've ever owned a dog, you won't be surprised to learn they have around 100 different facial expressions, most of them made with their ears.

Brain teaser

Write each answer in a clockwise direction around its clue number in the grid. When you have finished, the central blue hexagons will reveal the surname of a famous inventor.

1 Icy
2 Pay no attention to
3 Distance from end to end
4 Heavy downpour
5 Unpowered aircraft
6 Completely quiet

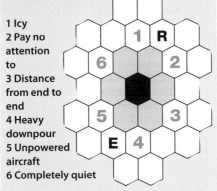

My perfect pet

NAME: **Belle**
AGE: **21 months**
OWNER: **Jasmine Stevens, aged 10**
PET LIKES: **Walks, toys, having her family around and all food**
PET HATES: **Being alone and loud noises, especially fireworks**
HUMAN TRAITS: **Eats fish on a Friday night and bacon and sausage on Sundays**

Recipe of the week

ORANGE GINGERBREAD MEN

Makes: 16
Preparation time: 10 mins
Cooking time: 12-15 mins

Gluten free

275g (10oz) gluten-free flour
1 dessert spoon ground ginger
½ tsp xanthan gum
1 tsp bicarbonate of soda
1 orange, zested
25g (1oz) stem ginger, finely chopped
75g (3oz) butter
50g (2oz) dark brown sugar
2 tbsp golden syrup
175g (6oz) icing sugar
25ml (1floz) warm water

1 Preheat the oven to 190°C/375°F/Gas Mark 5 and line 2 baking trays.

2 Sieve the gluten-free flour, ground ginger, xanthan gum and bicarbonate of soda into a mixing bowl, then add the orange zest and stem ginger.

3 Heat the butter, sugar and golden syrup. Stir until the sugar has dissolved, then pour into the flour mix. Beat until thoroughly combined and a firm dough has formed. Chill for 30 mins.

4 Roll out the dough to 4mm (¼in) thick. Cut out the gingerbread shapes and place on the baking trays.

5 Bake in the oven for 12-15 mins or until firm and golden brown, then turn out on to a cooling tray.

6 Once cool, decorate with coloured icing and decorations of your choice.

Credit: Udis Gluten Free

18 MONDAY

19 TUESDAY

20 WEDNESDAY

21 THURSDAY

22 FRIDAY

23 SATURDAY

24 SUNDAY

Express delivery

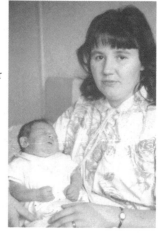

My neighbour and I were both pregnant at the same time and our babies were due on December 3, 1965. At this time it was very difficult to have a home birth, but fortunately a friend of an aunt was a midwife so we were able to plan our home births. On December 7, now overdue, our neighbours, my husband and I sat talking until late wondering when our babies would make an appearance.

My husband duly left for work at 5.30am the next morning. Our other neighbour (who was going to call the midwife for me), called round at 7.30am to see if I was all right. I said I was fine but had to dash upstairs to the toilet. Just as I got there I had a sharp pain and out came my 9.2lb son! I shouted down to my neighbour and said that the baby had arrived.

She dashed back home to ask her husband to go and phone the midwife at once. At that time we did not have home telephones, so he had to dash to the village payphone next to the shops. The midwife (who lived in the next village) arrived saying she hadn't even had time to put her corset on! At 10am that morning, my husband came home for his break and I typed a report for him. My neighbour ended up going into hospital to have her son the following Sunday.

Janet Emery, Walsall, W Mids

Animal magic

Would you agree to be treated by Dr Sheep? Perhaps it's not as baa-rmy as it sounds – sheep have been known to self-medicate by eating specific plants that will cure their ailments.

Brain teaser

Enter the pairs of letters from the list below into the circles, so that each line running through the central circle produces a six-letter word.

BA
BO
CY
DY
IN
KI
LA
NO
ON
RG
RN
SH
UR

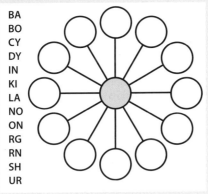

My perfect pet

NAME: **Teddy Bear**
AGE: **10**
OWNER: **Rosemary Medland**
PET LIKES: **Sleeping on owner's bed with his two step brothers**
PET HATES: **Dogs barking, cats meowing or babies crying on TV**
HUMAN TRAITS: **Loves lots of fuss and hugs. Also fond of a biscuit with his tea**

Recipe of the week

MINCEMEAT BROWNIES

Makes: 12
Preparation time: 15 mins
Cooking time: 45 mins

200g (7oz) dark chocolate cut into small pieces
200g (7oz) unsalted butter cubed
4 large eggs
300g (11oz) sugar
1 tsp vanilla extract
Zest of 1 clementine or orange
130g (4oz) flour
55g (2oz) cocoa powder
150g 5oz) mincemeat

1 Preheat the oven to 180°C/350°F/Gas Mark 4. Line a baking tin. Chop the chocolate into small chunks and place with butter in a bowl over a pan of simmering water to melt. Leave to cool.

2 Whisk the eggs and sugar. Add a little of the melted chocolate into the eggs and whisk, then add all the chocolate, vanilla, clementine zest and mix. Sift the flour and cocoa then fold in.

3 Fold in the mincemeat and transfer the batter to the tin. Bake for 40-45 mins. The brownies are ready when firm on top but soft to the touch. Test after 40 mins - if batter is too wet bake for a further 5-10 mins.

4 Pull the brownies out of the tin and cool. Cut into triangle shapes.

5 Finely chop the chocolate. Heat the cream and golden syrup until it bubbles. Remove from heat. Stir in the chocolate. Drizzle over the brownies and add sprinkles.
Credit: www.ao.com/life

25 MONDAY

26 TUESDAY

27 WEDNESDAY

28 THURSDAY

29 FRIDAY

30 SATURDAY

31 SUNDAY

Freezing memories of home

When I was a little girl in the late Forties we had some extremely cold winters. Some of my earliest memories are of the shock of stepping out of bed on to chilly lino. After the end of the war, when lino became available again and he could afford it, my father used it to cover the bare floorboards in our bedrooms. The photo shows our snow-covered garden as seen through our Crittall windows which were often patterned with frost on icy mornings.

I used to rush downstairs to the cosy kitchenette where, from November through to March, we dressed and undressed, washed, cooked and listened to the radio. Our coke boiler would have been riddled to provide us with heat and warm water. A kettle was set on top to boil.

Our 'best' room only had an open fire on Saturdays and Sundays. When I was old enough, my task was to keep the grate clean, lay the fire and light it. (We had to be very tidy indeed because the cat wanted some space, too!) The ashes from the grate were deposited on the garden path.

Every night, well-wrapped stone hot-water bottles were placed in our beds to warm them up before we got in. As many bedclothes as possible were piled on top – including our cardigans!

Another exceptionally cold winter that stands out in my memory was in 1962-63. I still have a black-and-white photograph taken of the Thames frozen over at Staines.
Priscilla Odell, Middlesex

Top tip

The Christmas party season may lead to a few late nights in a row. To reduce puffiness and redness around your eyes, don't opt for an expensive cream but instead use cooled green tea bags and leave on your eyes for 15 minutes. You'll soon look fresh-faced and ready for the next round of festivities.

Brain teaser

Each number in the grid indicates the number of trees in its adjacent squares. No tree can be horizontally, vertically or diagonally adjacent to another and no tree can appear in the same square as a number. Can you work out where all the trees are planted? We've placed one to help you get going.

1			1				2	
	2		1			1		
					1		2	1
2		2		1				
			2		3			2
		1				🌲	2	
		2						
2				1		2		1
	2		3					
							2	

My perfect pet

NAME: **Star**
AGE: **7**
OWNER: **Jenny Cripps**
PET LIKES: **Licking Jenny's head after washing her hair and sleeping on her shoulder**
PET HATES: **Vacuum cleaners and lawnmowers**
HUMAN TRAITS: **Enjoys eating crisps (but only occasionally)**

Recipe of the week

STIR-FRY TURKEY

Serves: 4
Preparation time: 20 mins
Cooking time: 5 mins

6 tbsp olive oil
1 small onion, finely chopped
2x 250g (9oz) packs microwavable brown basmati rice
2 eggs, beaten
50g (2oz) baby leaf spinach
350g-450g (12oz-1lb) turkey breast, cut into 2cm strips
4 tbsp reduced-salt soy sauce or tamari (if you want gluten free)
4 tbsp tomato ketchup
4 tbsp vinegar
Salt and pepper

1 Heat 2 tbsp, then add the onion and cook for 3-4 mins. Heat the rice for 2 mins, then break up the rice and leave aside.

2 Once the onions are cooked set aside and heat 2 more tbsp of oil to the pan. Once hot pour in the beaten egg and stir quickly, so the eggs cook. Add the spinach to the cooked egg, then return the onions to the pan and warm until the spinach wilts. Add the rice, stir and season.

3 Meanwhile, heat the last 2 tbsp of oil and add the turkey, fry for 2 mins. Add the soy sauce (or tamari), ketchup and vinegar and cook the turkey. Season well. Spoon the egg rice into bowls and top with the turkey and sauce.
Credit: Phil Vickery www.kikkoman.co.uk

It's time to

Jane asked: "What on earth have you got in here?" as she picked up Sally's suitcase and carried it to the car. "We're only going away for four days, not four months."

"Just a few jumpers and a fleecy throw in case the cottage is a bit draughty," Sally said, locking the front door and following her sister down the path. "And my books, of course."

"You've brought a case full of books?" Jane closed the boot.

"Hardly a whole case," Sally laughed as she settled into the passenger seat. "But I did go to the library to stock up."

Jane tutted and shook her head.

"Why are you surprised? We agreed that a winter break in the country was the perfect way to unwind and catch up on some reading. No husbands or grandchildren demanding our attention. I love them all dearly but I'm really looking forward to have a few days to myself."

Jane said: "Me too, but you won't catch me lugging around a pile of books when I've got my tablet and can download all the books I want at the click of a button."

"Robert has been hinting that he would buy me one for my birthday, but to be honest I'm not that

---

"No need, I did an online shop before we left and it should all be delivered here later this afternoon"

---

keen. I prefer the feel of a real book in my hand."

"It's time you moved into the twenty-first century, sis. Have you got everything? Can we set off now?"

Sally clapped her hand to her mouth. "Oh, I've just remembered! I've left the route directions on the hall table. Robert wrote them down for us."

Jane drove off. "Don't worry - we don't need them. This car has satnav." She pressed a switch and a clipped female voice instructed: "Turn right at the next junction."

Jane said: "There you are. We know exactly where we're going."

Sally smiled. "I should hope so. We're only at the end of my street!"

They spent the two-hour drive catching up on family news and reminiscing about holidays they'd had when they were growing up. Eventually, they turned into a narrow lane that led to the cottage that was to be their holiday home.

"It's lovely," Sally said when they went inside and gazed at the stunning view from the large window in the lounge. "How did you find it? Did someone recommend it to you?"

"No. I searched online and found a website that lets you do a virtual tour of the properties. Much better than relying on those flattering photos you get in a brochure."

Sally agreed. "I wish we could have done that years ago when we went on holiday with Mum and Dad. Do you remember that caravan in Wales? The roof leaked and the cows from the next field came to visit us whenever we went out to play."

Jane laughed at the memory. "But it didn't matter. Everyone was so friendly. It was one of the best holidays we had, even though there was no TV and it was a five-minute walk to the toilet block."

After they had unpacked, Sally suggested a walk into the village to stock up on food.

"No need!" Jane replied. "I did an online shop before we left and it should all be delivered here later this afternoon. I even remembered those iced-lemon cookies you like. I doubt you'd get them in the village shop."

While they were preparing supper the sisters discussed what they might do the next day.

"There's a nature reserve a few miles from here," Sally said, reading a leaflet from the information folder. "I wouldn't mind going there if it isn't raining."

Jane said: "I've got a weather app on my phone. I'll check it later."

"Or we could just watch the local forecast on TV," Sally smiled.

move on

Story by Elizabeth McKay
Illustration by Kate Davies

When they sat down to eat they discovered that one of the table legs was wobbly. "Better not lean too heavily on it," Jane warned, but the soup had already splashed out of Sally's bowl on to the tablecloth.

After they had mopped it up, Sally said: "I must buy a few postcards to send to the grandchildren."

"I never send postcards these days. I'll send my lot a text."

Sally protested: "I don't think it's quite the same. And they love getting something through the post."

"Like I said, Sally, it's the twenty-first century. Time you got to grips with technology," Jane said as she leaned over to top up their wine glasses. The table gave another lurch and red wine spilled everywhere.

"I'll get the cloth again," she said jumping up and disappearing into the kitchen. When she came back she was surprised to find Sally sitting with both elbows resting comfortably on a steady table.

"You fixed it?"

"Not me," Sally grinned. "John Grisham."

Jane stared at her sister. "I think that one glass of wine has gone to your head."

Sally laughed and pointed at the table leg which was resting on the paperback of John Grisham's latest bestseller.

"Technology is all fine and dandy," she said smugly, "but you couldn't have done that with your tablet, could you?"

Poetry Corner

The New Alphabet

By Jean Williams

A is for arthritis

B is the bad back

C is for chest pains, perhaps cardiac

D is for dental decay and decline

E is for eyesight, can't read the top line

F is for fissure and fluid retention

G is for gas, which I'd rather not mention

H is high-blood pressure, I'd rather it low

I is incisions, with scars you can't show

J is for joints, out of socket, won't mend

K is for knees that crack when they bend

L's for libido, what happened to sex?

M is for memory, I forget what comes next...

N is neuralgia, is nerves way down low

O is for osteo, the bones that don't grow

P is prescriptions, I have quite a few

Just give me a pill and I'll be good as new

Q is for queasy, is it fatal or flu?

R is for reflux, one meal turns into two

S is for sleepless nights, counting my fears,

T is for tinnitus, there's bells in my ears

U is for urinary, big troubles with flow.

V is for vertigo, that's dizzy you know.

W is for worry. Now what's going round?

X is for X-ray and what might be found.

Y is another year I'm left here behind

Z's for the zest I still have - in my mind.

We took down the black-out curtains & prepared for life in the new Welfare State, but what else do you remember about this decade?

1 Who wrote and starred as a naval captain in the wartime film In Which We Serve?

2 What did the initials ITMA stand for in the radio comedy show that ran from 1939 to 1949?

3 Who married her handsome naval officer on November 20, 1947?

4 Who was the health secretary when the National Health Service was launched in July 1948?

5 In which year did Christian Dior's New Look take the fashion world by storm?

6 What was the name given to the set of clothes that servicemen received when they returned to civilian life?

7 Whose diary was first broadcast on the BBC Light Programme on January 5, 1948?

8 What was the name of the famous polar bear cub born at London Zoo in November 1949?

PICS: ALAMY

Remember the Forties?

9 Which forces' sweetheart sang 'Lay Down Your Arms and Surrender to Mine'?

10 By what name was radio presenter Derek McCulloch better known to children?

11 In which famous stately home near Oxford was wartime leader Winston Churchill born?

12 Which distinguished cricketer also played football for Arsenal?

13 Which crime writer was investigated by MI5 after the publication in 1941 of her thriller N or M?

14 Whose catchphrase was "What's on the table, Mabel?"

15 During the war, what did the letters ARP stand for?

16 In which country was Ab Fab star Joanna Lumley born in May 1946?

17 Cyril Joad and Julian Huxley were panel members of which popular radio programme?

18 Who became prime minister after Labour's landslide victory in the 1945 election?

19 In which year did the film The Lost Weekend starring Ray Milland win the Oscar for Best Picture?

20 In 1945, which Gainsborough film about a highwayman made actress Margaret Lockwood a star?

21 Root vegetables were the main ingredients of which pie, named after a wartime Minister of Food?

22 Which historical romance by Kathleen Winsor was considered shocking when it was published in 1944?

23 The radio programme Kitchen Front was presented by which cookery writer who preferred to be known as a home economist?

24 Jokingly claimed to stand for Every Night Something Awful, what did the acronym ENSA really represent?

25 Who wrote The Castle of Adventure, published in 1946?

Answers on page 182

Scaling new

Abigail Williams was looking for a fresh challenge 23 years ago – but a charity climb proved a real up and down experience

I was bursting with confidence and felt on top of the world. Well, actually I almost was. I'd just reached the summit of Ben Nevis – at 4,406ft it's the highest mountain in Britain. Not only that but it meant I'd raised hundreds of pounds for cystic fibrosis sufferers.

It was 1993. My life was rather humdrum working in a steady nine-to-five job in London's Square Mile and I was still single. I was needing a fresh challenge when I saw an advert asking for volunteers to undertake a sponsored charity 'walk' up Ben Nevis. The charity would organise transport, food and accommodation. All we had to supply was enthusiasm, some sponsorship from friends and family, and strong legs! I dusted off my walking boots, dug out my woolly hat, gloves and a warm sweater and squeezed them all into a borrowed rucksack. It was a crisp October morning and as I neared the designated pick-up point I began to feel nervous. I was alone, and suddenly feared everyone would be with friends. Thankfully, my fears were mostly unfounded. Lots of people were milling around, but many were alone too.

I got chatting to some of the other single women. As the coach sped along the motorway we learnt about each other's lives and reasons for wanting to take up the challenge. By the time we reached the Scottish border there was a real sense of camaraderie. By now darkness had descended and the huge, dark silhouettes of the mountains eerily surrounded us as we approached our hotel in Fort William. That night, after a de-briefing by the organisers and an early dinner, I massaged my legs with a blend of special oils in preparation for the next day's ascent.

At six the following morning, the mountains were still resting behind low cloud and mist

> **By the time we reached the Scottish border there was a real sense of camaraderie**

and in spite of the early hour I breakfasted on bacon and eggs and hoped this was not a huge mistake! An hour later our group of 20 to 70 year olds of all shapes and sizes stood at the base of Ben Nevis in silent awe as we looked up at the challenge ahead, each secretly hoping we'd make the top. I started the walk in leggings, sweatshirt, walking boots and chunky socks but an hour into the ascent I was boiling and was sure I would never need the woollies I'd brought or the windproof jacket that had been supplied.

We set off across a small bridge before joining the undulating path that teased us into the ascent. The weather brightened and it was amazing to see our surroundings clearly now; the air was pure and the landscape breathtaking. As we climbed up

Plenty of enthusiasm was the main requirement for tackling Ben Nevis

heights

Abigail faced up to the challenge and remembers the experience as one of her greatest moments

and up, scrabbling over jagged rocks in places, I stopped now and then to take photos and a much-needed breather! At one o'clock we all sat down with the packed lunch we'd been given.

Then, the ascent really really started. The weather became increasingly cold and I was grateful to put on my woollies and jacket. As the path became rockier and rockier I began to feel weary, lagging towards the back but was encouraged by one of the guides. "Keep going, you can't give up now," he said and somehow it had the desired effect. I pushed on, my feet crunching over the light snow that was now scattered over the path.

Although the rest of me was warmly clad my face now began to feel raw from the wind, but

just as I thought I couldn't take another step, the mountain summit came into view. It was the incentive I needed. With aching legs, back and soles of my feet, I kept putting one foot in front of the other until at last I was atop the summit. It was exhilarating. Everyone hugged and posed for the group shot to prove we had done it!

Just when I thought it was time for the easy part, my nightmare really began. As the descent became more vertical my toes rammed into the front of my boots and it became increasingly painful with each descending step. I untied and retied my boots to give my ankles better support, and rest my feet, but to no avail. Close to tears I realised there was only one

thing for it, I had no option but to run down that mountain to minimise the length of time I'd be in agony. And so I did, leaping and running over rock slabs, whizzing past everyone and everything and despite the ever-increasing possibility of ending up spread-eagled over the rocks, I survived and made it back to base a whole hour before the rest of the group.

For weeks after, I felt I could conquer the world. Despite bruised legs, black toenails and my muscles aching every time I went downstairs, I felt a huge sense of achievement. Not only had I faced the challenge but I knew my sponsorship money was going towards helping people with much greater life challenges to overcome. I still count that experience as one of my greatest moments.

Go Granddad

Martin would do anything for Poppy, but is he up to her latest challenge?

Martin swallowed. So this was Harry Carter's dad. Poppy had made it clear that Harry Carter's dad must not be allowed to win the pancake race. Wearing her most earnest expression, she had explained: "Because Harry Carter is a twit, Granddad."

Martin had reminded Poppy that we are all twits sometimes and that Harry's dad had as much right to win as anyone else.

It had all started one morning when Hannah, Martin's daughter, had stopped by for coffee and a slice of ginger cake after dropping Poppy off at school.

"Mmm. This cake is so good, Dad. You've missed your vocation – you should have been on Masterchef." She licked her fingers. "You are not by any chance secretly good at sport as well, are you?"

"Afraid not," Martin said. "Having a lifelong limp has never exactly been an asset. I had a go at shot putting once and only just missed my own foot."

Hannah wasn't about to give up. "But on a scale of one to ten, if one is unconscious and ten is Olympic standard?"

Martin sat back in his chair and folded his arms. "In that case, two."

Hannah looked dejected. "Gosh, that's terrible." Then a flicker of hope crossed her face: "But you can make pancakes, right?"

"Poppy's really disappointed. All the other parents can make it. And you know what it's like at that age."

Martin sat up straight again. "Ah, now you're talking."

Hannah explained that the school was having a fundraising event but Poppy's dad couldn't get time off work to take part in the fathers' pancake race. A substitute was needed.

"What? Running, me?" Martin said desperately. "No way!"

"Poppy's really disappointed. All the other parents can make it. And you know what it's like at that age."

They had two weeks. Training would require a two-pronged attack – perfecting the tastiest pancake and being able to toss it while running as fast as possible.

"You can do it, Dad," Hannah said. "How hard can it be?"

Martin didn't answer, but he knew it was time to stand up and be counted. This was for Poppy, after all.

Making the pancake was no problem. Martin could make thin lacy ones, thick fluffy ones, spicy ones, fruity ones. Hannah and Poppy dropped by regularly to sample them.

Martin said: "I think the thicker ones are best. I don't want one that's going to blow away in the wind when I toss it."

"Ah yes, the tossing. How's that going?" Hannah asked.

"Yes, show us, Granddad," Poppy watched him expectantly.

"Right. Give the chef some room. The perfect flip is all in the wrist action." Martin gripped the pan, swirled, then tossed. "Ooops!"

"That nearly landed in my lap," Hannah said.

Now here he was, waiting for the whistle to start the race. Standing next to him was Harry Carter's dad, a man with the physique of Mr Universe. Martin tried to give Poppy a reassuring smile but she was distracted by a giggling boy who was pointing at Martin while doing a silly, stiff-legged walk.

'So that's Harry', he thought. 'He does look a right little twit'.

The rules were that contestants had to toss their pancakes twice, once at the beginning of the race and once just before the end. Dropping your pancake meant instant disqualification.

The whistle went and Harry set off, limping along at a pretty good pace considering he was at least twenty years older than most of his rivals. As they neared the finishing line, he was bringing up the rear while up in front Harry's dad surged forward and broke the tape.

As he swivelled round to spot Poppy in the crowd, Martin's gammy leg gave way. He flung out his arms to save himself and his pancake somersaulted through the air, landing squarely on the head of the triumphant Mr Universe.

go!

Story by Jan Halstead
Illustration by Kate Davies

The crowd, who had warmed to him, gave a rousing cheer, but Martin had lost the race and, worse than that, he'd let Harry's dad win. Clambering wearily to his feet, he was relieved to see a smiling Poppy running towards him. She flung her arms around his legs. "Well done, Granddad!"

He stroked her hair. "I'm sorry, lovey. I never was any good at sport."

"That's okay. Mum says you might have come last but you did it in style!" She smirked at Harry who was taking a photo of his dad with a pancake draped over his head.

"I really must apologise," Martin said, holding out a hand to Mr Universe.

"Oh, please don't worry," said Harry's dad, pulling off a piece of pancake and popping it in his mouth. "This is amazing. Blueberry, isn't it? And something else?"

"A smidgen of apple purée," Martin told him.

Harry's dad licked his lips appreciatively. "Delicious. I can only make plain ones and they are like rubber."

"I think I know where you are going wrong there," Martin said, lifting the remains of the pancake off his rival's head. "It's all in the mixing. You mustn't overwork it."

"Well, that explains it. I used to play county cricket and I've certainly got a strong right arm."

"Ah well, when it comes to pancakes, it probably doesn't do to be too athletic."

Deep in conversation, the two men headed for the tea tent while Poppy and Harry giggled happily over the photos of his dad wearing a pancake hat.

Poetry Corner

Ode to the mighty pen

By Victoria Calvert

When I went to school, I wrote with pen and ink.
I became ink monitor during my first year.
So proud I was and a bit strict I think;
Nibs replaced, one to each pen,
the rule was very clear.
Ink mixed each day, sometimes black,
mostly blue
Always hard to produce the correct hue!

Then the fountain pen, inky blots everywhere!
We were taught to write in that 'eyetalic' fashion.
It looked very nice giving our words real flair,
Handwriting became a prize-winning passion.
Growing up meant a typewriter,
used with great success.
Carbon-paper fingers, an inky blue mess.

A new word processor; oh what a treat!
Tap in a word - don't bother about spelling!
Autocorrect made your prose look so neat,
Did it for you without any telling.
The revolution came, the ultimate PC.
Oh internet, how much do I love thee!

Programmes and apps all there; easy to research,
A laptop so handy to use anywhere;
Charged battery, switch on and a comfy perch.
All around us inspiration and flair.
Relying on technology do we get smug,
Occasionally should we pull the plug?

Aargh, the laptop's not working, won't switch on.
I don't know why and which button to press.
The man thinks that the hard drive
might have gone.
How much of my work lost? I can only guess.
Submission dates so very near; here I go then
Back where I started... with paper and pen.

We watched the Queen's Coronation on the next-door neighbour's TV set and missed our menfolk away on National Service, but what else do you remember about this decade?

1 Which footballer had the nickname The Wizard of Dribble?

2 In which year were ID cards abolished and a charge of one shilling on prescriptions introduced?

3 Said to be the longest running soap opera in the world, which radio series was first broadcast on January 1, 1951?

4 What were the first names of the sisters who had a chart-topping hit with You Belong to Me in 1956?

5 Which lovable but accident-prone comedian was said to be Charlie Chaplin's favourite clown?

6 In 1957, who replaced Anthony Eden as Prime Minister?

7 The Skylon was a feature of which national exhibition held in the summer of 1951?

8 Christopher Trace and Leila Williams were the first presenters of which children's TV programme first aired in 1958?

9 In 1953 tea bags were first introduced to the UK by which company?

Remember the Fifties?

PICS: ALAMY

10 Which newspaper had a comic strip featuring Andy Capp and his long-suffering wife, Florrie?

11 In 1955 which chain of grocery shops opened its first supermarket in the London suburb of Streatham?

12 Who was the singer dubbed the Tigress from Tiger Bay?

13 Who designed the embroidered white satin gown the Queen wore for her Coronation?

14 Which down-on-his-luck comedian lived at 23 Railway Cuttings, East Cheam?

15 What was the destination of several thousand protest marchers who set off from Trafalgar Square over the Easter weekend of 1958?

16 The Shadows were the backing group for which British pop singer?

17 Launched in 1959 and marketed as the Austin Seven and the Morris Mini-Minor, the original Mini was the brain child of which famous designer?

18 Who was the British army officer who led the British expedition that reached the summit of Mount Everest on May 29, 1954?

19 The football anthem You'll Never Walk Alone was sung in which 1956 film starring Jennifer Jones and Gordon MacRae?

20 Who played the wartime heroine Violette Szabo in the 1958 film Carve Her Name with Pride?

21 Why did Roger Bannister make headlines in May 1954?

22 Which religious leader went into exile in 1959 in protest at the Chinese annexation of Tibet?

23 How did two monkeys named Able and Baker shoot to fame in 1959?

24 Which American crooner had a number one hit in the UK with Just Walkin' in the Rain?

25 Who did Jacqueline Lee Bouvier marry in a ceremony on Rhode Island in September 1953?

Were you right? Turn to page 182 for all the answers

Dad was an

For Gwyn Grocott, travelling the world was just a normal part of life growing up – including being chased by lions!

I cannot believe that I don't remember flying in a plane with the doors open to let in some air! But, my sister who is three years older than me, and remembers so much more than I do, assures me that is what happened. The year was 1958, I was eight years old and we had set off from Stansted airport. My memory of the airport then is that it was just a wooden hut. We were flying, eventually, to Singapore where Dad would be waiting for us, but it would take us three days to reach it.

Dad was in the RAF and whenever we got posted he had to go a few months earlier until a married quarter became available for us all. This was my childhood – and it was a happy one, moving every few years and living in some exotic places. Add to that the fact that Dad was a

In Aden the family lived on a beach

padre – and also a ventriloquist and magician – and we had a pretty unusual and exciting upbringing.

When we returned from Singapore – on a troop ship this time – we stayed on board for a full three weeks and had to attend school. We travelled through the Suez Canal and at the time I was playing Happy Families with a friend. Mum kept pestering me to come and look at

---

Mum kept pestering me to come and look at the pyramids... but of course, at the time, Happy Families was more appealing

---

the pyramids saying, "You might never see them again." Of course, at the time, Happy Families was more appealing. But Mum was right and I've never set eyes on them from that day to this.

We were posted to Aden, then still a North African British colony, where we first lived in the crater of an extinct volcano and Dad's church was a cave. When we moved, we still lived on a beach. I remember the sandstorms, plagues of locusts and, often, the unbearable heat. We had to be admitted to hospital for every little thing. I started school there and we used to be driven on an armed lorry. Mum became very ill with kidney stones and had to

be invalided back home, so our stay in Aden was shorter than it should have been.

The risks we took seem unbelievable now. When we were still there, we took a trip further into Africa and stayed with the parents of the former LibDem leader, David Steele. One time, we went to a game reserve and the car broke down, so we had to get out and push – watched by lions. We also went for a picnic and had a lovely day playing silly games, unaware that the native Mau Mau insurgents had killed some white colonialists in the same area only a few days earlier.

Apart from Singapore and Aden, we also lived in Germany and different parts of England. This meant always having to up sticks, start new schools and make new friends, but I can't remember that being a problem. Because Dad always had to go ahead of us, Mum would pack up and take the rest of the family back to Wales to stay with an auntie who lived in the valleys, while she waited for the call to follow Dad. I just loved these times. Mum came from a large family and we had to go to the village school for the time we were there. I developed an eye problem so had to have time off just before the summer holidays and then during that holiday we set off for Singapore. A few months

RAF padre

Gwyn and her family had many adventures while travelling around the world to exotic places

later my auntie wrote to say the school bobby had been round as I wasn't attending school! Mum had forgotten to inform them that I wasn't returning after the summer.

In England we lived in Somerset, Buckinghamshire, Norfolk and Hampshire. RAF stations are always in the country so I grew up climbing trees, making dens in the woods and with lots of freedom. In Somerset and Norfolk we also lived near the sea so had all the beach fun you could ask for. My last school was in Germany – a boarding school. We had no choice as there were no local schools. I hated being away from Mum and Dad and home, but looking back it wasn't a bad place and I am still very good friends with girls from those days.

We travelled the world, saw amazing sights and had wonderful adventures. But it didn't matter where I was as long as I had Mum, Dad and my brother and sister. Home was home wherever we were and it's only now that I'm old that I think, wow, I really did live in those exotic places and see and experience so many extraordinary things.

In the merry

Jenny doesn't share Stephen's enthusiasm for his new hobby

Jenny murmured: "You look...um...great," as Stephen pranced around the lounge, the bells on his knees jingling merrily.

"I'm going to be dancing in the town square on the May bank holiday, Jen," he said.

"Sounds brilliant," Jenny forced a smile. Morris dancing wasn't her kind of thing and Stephen's euphoria, since he had joined the local group two months earlier, merely served to emphasise her own low spirits. It was quite a shock to see him behaving so flamboyantly as he had always been the introverted one of the two of them.

But Jenny couldn't help feeling a bit envious of the sparkle in his blue eyes. He had clearly found a hobby he truly enjoyed, while she felt she didn't do much with her life these days. She wondered if she was turning into a forty-something bore. Was that how Stephen saw her?

On an impulse, she heard herself saying: "Maybe I should come along?"

He gave her a lopsided smile. "Are you sure it's really you, Jen?"

She instantly wondered if he actually wanted her there. Anyway, he was right – it wasn't her scene, although she had loved dancing when she was young. As a child she had gone to ballet lessons

---

"Jen just wished that Morris dancing gave her the same buzz it clearly gave him"

---

and in her 20s enjoyed disco dancing with her girlfriends. But it was a long time since Jenny had bopped happily around her handbag.

Stephen picked up some brightly-coloured handkerchiefs and pranced about the lounge with the dog barking at his heels.

Jenny said half-heartedly: "I might like it. You never know."

"Well, if you want to give it a go..." he said a little cautiously.

A week later they arrived at the village hall. It was bustling with men and women dressed traditionally in white, some wearing hats garlanded with flowers. A number of them were dancing in squares, practising routines, while others knocked sticks together or flicked handkerchiefs. One man

was playing a fiddle.

Jenny froze in the doorway – this really wasn't her idea of a good night out – but the laughter and music drew her in. She perched on the edge of a chair, keeping one eye on the exit.

"You go and enjoy yourself, Stephen," she urged. "I'll just sit here and watch for a bit."

"Are you sure?" he asked, but didn't hang around for an answer. Jen just wished that Morris dancing gave her the same buzz it clearly gave him.

A little later she caught a glimpse of him in the crowd chatting to a woman in her 30s. Stephen smiled as the woman reached over and picked a stray piece of cotton from his shirt.

Suddenly, Jen felt drab, sitting alone wearing jeans and an old jumper.

"Hi!"

She looked up to see one of the dancers towering over her.

He said: "I'm Alfie, the foreman. I teach the dances."

Alfie had chocolate brown eyes, a bushy beard and the widest smile she had ever seen.

"I'm Jenny."

"Are you hoping to join the side?"

"Maybe, yes."

"Well, don't be shy. We're a friendly lot. My wife started the side many years ago."

Jenny glanced around the room, trying to spot the woman who was married to this charming, if slightly crazy-looking man.

Guessing her thoughts, Alfie said: "She passed away ten years ago."

"I'm sorry to hear that," Jenny said, but Alfie was already heading off. Glancing over his shoulder, he said: "Well, are you coming?"

Jenny left her seat and went over to where Stephen was standing on his own. He looked surprised. "Are you going to join in, Jen?"

Feeling suddenly nervous, she nodded cautiously. "I think so."

But when the music started, Jenny found herself dancing with abandon. By the end of the evening she was wearing bells on her knees, flicking handkerchiefs, and laughing in a way that she hadn't laughed for a long time

As they headed for the car park, Stephen smiled. "I'm glad you had a good time. You look brighter

month of May

Story by Amanda Brittany
Illustration by Kate Davies

than I've seen you for ages."

Amazed that Morris dancing could be so much fun, Jen said: "I actually feel more like the old me!"

When Stephen opened the car door for her, Jenny gave him a sideways look and asked: "Who is she?"

"Who?"

"The woman you were talking to, of course."

"She's a friend, that's all, Jen," he said, his cheeks colouring.

As he started the engine, she persisted: "Well, she looked like more than just a friend to me."

Turning, he met her enquiring look. "Okay. She is more than just a friend."

"I knew it!" Jenny smiled broadly. She was delighted that her shy brother had finally found someone special. He would be 40 next birthday and she had begun to despair of him meeting the right woman.

As they drove home, he said: "How about you, sis? I saw you talking to Alfie."

It was Jenny's turn to blush. "Well, he's very nice."

"Very nice?" Stephen teased.

Jenny wasn't sure if she was ready for a relationship just yet. Her recent divorce had been a painful process that had left her distrustful of life. Too distrustful she realised now, but Morris dancing, of all things, had put a smile on her face and given her hope for the future.

Poetry Corner

Dance For Life

By Sharon Boothroyd

Hey cool cats, let's take a chance
Here's a poem all about dance
This is for you, if dance is your thing
A raunchy can-can to a highland fling

Listen up, here's what I say
Dance is true, from tap to ballet
Tie those shoes - get in the mood
A ballroom waltz or an American smooth?

We feel so alive
As we step into jive
We love to dance a cheeky rumba
And don't forget our weekly Zumba!

It takes two for a lover's tango
Shimmy and glide to jaunty tempo
Allow the music to ebb and flow
Join a disco beat and go, go, go!

All of us dancing in a line
The rhythm really is so fine
Slide and step - now clap hands
It's symmetry, you understand

At hoe-down time, we turn and twist
Oh, you stumbled there and missed!
Raw rap, dance street hip-hop
Stomp along to rock and pop

High leg kicks and spin around
Lift your feet right off the ground
A run, a jump and a little skip
There's a fancy double back flip!

It's good for us to dance together
A graceful duo, time-locked forever
Dance for life, a rich melody
Spirited away to harmony.

We wore mini skirts and had teenage crushes on The Beatles or The Stones, but what else do you remember about this decade?

1 What is the full name of the conservation body that was founded in April 1961 with a panda as its emblem?

2 Which country house by the River Thames became notorious because of the part it played in the Profumo Affair?

3 The 1961 film Breakfast At Tiffany's starred Audrey Hepburn - but who wrote the book on which it was based?

4 As the first Dr Who, which actor travelled in the Tardis and did battle with the Daleks?

5 Founded as a broadsheet in 1964, which newspaper was relaunched as a tabloid in 1969?

6 Who arrived at the church in a green Rolls Royce for her marriage to Maurice Gibb in February 1969?

7 What was the name of the Welsh mining village in which 116 children were killed when a slag heap collapsed on their school?

8 What was the name of the snail in the children's TV programme The Magic Roundabout?

Remember the Sixties?

9 Which brand of crisps introduced cheese-and-onion flavour in 1962?

10 In which year did George Lazenby take over as 007 in the film On Her Majesty's Service?

11 Which Yorkshire-born Prime Minister caused controversy by awarding The Beatles MBEs?

12 What was the name of the oil tanker that ran aground in March 1967, polluting Cornish beaches and causing the death of thousands of sea birds?

13 In 1968 who returned to a hero's welcome in Portsmouth after sailing around the world in 354 days?

14 Buster Edwards hit the headlines after which notorious event that took place on the night of August 8, 1963?

15 Which black civil rights leader became the youngest person to receive the Nobel Peace Prize in 1964?

16 Designed to fly at twice the speed of sound, from which airport in France did Concorde make its first flight in March 1969?

17 What made South African surgeon Christian Barnard a household name in 1967?

18 Under which president did the United States become involved in the war in Vietnam?

19 Sandie Shaw won the Eurovision Song Contest with which song?

20 Who fought each other on the beaches of Brighton and Margate over Whitsun weekend, 1964?

21 Which bird became a media sensation when it escaped from London Zoo in March 1965 and took up residence in Regent's Park?

22 Also known as TW3, which satirical TV show was presented by David Frost and featured singer Millicent Martin?

23 What was the pen name of Dora Jessie Saint, who wrote Winter in Thrush Green, published in 1961?

24 Which actress starred with Cliff Richard in the film Summer Holiday, before finding fame as Alf Garnett's daughter?

25 Which 1961 bestseller by Harold Robbins was made into a film starring George Peppard and Carroll Baker?

Answers on page 182

PICS: ALAMY

That sweltering

Jackie Winter and partner chose the heatwave of 1976 to go on their first tandem cycling holiday around the Yorkshire Dales

It was the year when Brotherhood of Man triumphed at the Eurovision Song Contest with Save All Your Kisses for Me; inflation hovered at around 17 per cent and Denis Howell found himself appointed Minister For Drought. But I shall always remember 1976 as the year of my most memorable cycling holiday. Allan and I have friends who also ride a tandem and this was our first holiday together, when we were in our early 20s. We were camping in the Yorkshire Dales and everything had to be carried in a couple of panniers and a saddlebag. I could only take seven pairs of knickers but by wearing them inside out on the second day, I made them last a fortnight.

First we camped at Knaresborough, then moved on to Appletreewick. Our friends didn't eat meat and we quickly discovered that cooking for four with only two small billycans tested the imagination to the limit. Supper usually consisted of either fish fingers with tinned carrots or boil-in-the-bag cod and instant mash.

Funds were meagre but so were those boring rations, which was the reason for us treating ourselves to a modest meal at

---

Supper usually consisted of either fish fingers with tinned carrots or boil-in-the-bag cod

---

Appletreewick. The first pub we found was called the New Inn and, to our surprise, it was entirely non-smoking - unheard of in the Seventies. In we went, keen to spend an evening breathing unpolluted air. But we didn't stay long! Everyone looked old and depressed, the atmosphere was hushed and the barman glowered at us. So we scuttled out and made for the other pub around the corner, preferring to eat our supper in a bit of cheerful fug.

It was the last week of June and the country was starting to sizzle. Under the glare of a pitiless sun, we cycled to Hawes and toiled up Buttertubs Pass, while the Tarmac melted beneath our wheels. Any shady patch of road was welcomed joyfully and we were so thirsty it was difficult to ration the water in our cycling bottles, so it would last until the next campsite. I don't remember bottled water being available anywhere in 1976.

When we discovered the market town of Helmsley, with its open-air swimming pool, we wanted to stay there forever. It was total bliss, dunking our boiling bodies into the depth of that cool water. And that wasn't the extent of our self-indulgence. There was an Italian ice-cream parlour next to the swimming pool, with ice-cream sodas in no fewer than six exotic flavours.

While at Helmsley, we treated ourselves to the only posh meal of our holiday, at the Black Swan Hotel. With youthful cyclists' appetites, we demolished avocado with prawns, coq-au-vin, trout studded with almonds and double helpings of Black Forest gateau. Recklessly, we ordered one bottle of

summer

Jackie and Allan's white bri-nylon T-shirts proved to be so uncomfortable in the soaring temperatures that they had to throw them away

Liebfraumilch and another of Mateus Rosé. The bill for £17.50 sobered us up pretty smartly and heads down, we scuttled off without leaving a tip. As a junior library assistant, that sum represented more than half a week's wages for me.

It was only the prospect of immersing ourselves in the chilly waters of the North Sea that persuaded us to leave Helmsley and move on to Robin Hood's Bay. That day, the scorching sun almost defeated us and we toiled through the small villages of Great Fryup and Little Fryup in exhausted silence.

I was suffering badly from sunburn. My fair skin burnt quickly and in those days SPF was pretty much unheard of. We arrived at Robin Hood's Bay

too tired to do more than search out supper at a café near the campsite.

We spend the following day lazily in Whitby, eating fish and chips and reading newspapers. That was when we discovered we'd struggled through the Dale of Fryup on the hottest day ever recorded in Britain at the time, when the temperature soared to 96.6°F.

James Callaghan was urging a sweaty nation to bathe in only five inches of water. This message was reinforced by car stickers, badges and T-shirts, encouraging everyone to, "Save water, bath with a friend".

Allan and I could have used a couple of those T-shirts. We'd brought some with us that had come free with a bottle of Brut aftershave. They were

shiny white bri-nylon with the Brut logo printed centre-stage. It's hard to describe how uncomfortable we felt on the day we wore them. The material didn't absorb sweat at all and we just became hotter and smellier, until at last we gave up and threw them in the bin. With T-shirts rationed to only five for a fortnight, this was a severe blow.

On the train home, we compiled a list of unforgettable memories...

Whitby fish and chips; Helmsley swimming pool; our meal at the Black Swan Hotel and the heat. Most of all the relentless and overwhelming heat.

◆ *Life in Tandem, Tales of cycling travels, by Jackie Winter is available to buy on Amazon*

Busy doing

Can Sally cope with a change of routine?

Sally liked plans. She relied on them. Running family life efficiently wasn't easy and it was her methodical mind that got Sally through the daily challenge of looking after her husband and two teenage daughters.

Shopping lists, to-do lists and diaries aided her well-run life. She hadn't always been so organised. In the hazily remembered days before marriage and children she had been a dreamier person altogether.

Top of her list for today was food shopping. As she was going around the supermarket, her mobile rang. When she answered something in her husband's voice stopped her in her tracks.

"Sal?"

"Pete, what is it?"

"We're going to have to cancel our holiday. The contract I've been sweating over is finally mine!" He sounded jubilant. "I start work at the beginning of August."

"That's fantastic!" Sally recalled the many months he had spent planning and researching this major project.

Pete sounded relieved by her positive response. He went on: "The start date clashes with our holiday, so we'll just have to do something impromptu as soon as the girls break up from school."

"That's this week!"

"I know, but could you see if there is anything available?"

"Okay," Sally sighed.

They threw all their things haphazardly into the car, the girls plugged in their music and they were off

---

"Thanks for being such a good sport, love," Pete said, knowing how hard it was for his wife to deviate from her usual routine.

She finished her shopping, but her day had been shattered. Cancel the holiday? They had visited the same lodge for as many summers as she could remember and she always booked it for the following year as soon as they arrived.

When it came to packing, she knew exactly what was needed and did it all in advance. Badminton rackets, sun oil, wet suits, jumpers for chilly evenings - Sally had it all sorted.

What was Pete thinking when he used the word impromptu? Didn't he know that the first week of the summer holidays was bound to be fully booked everywhere?

"We'd like the same lodge, but two weeks earlier," she explained to the woman who ran the campsite. Sally's worst fears were confirmed when there was a long pause at the other end of the line before she replied: "Leave it with me."

But to her surprise, the woman did call back. "Mrs Naylor? I've had a cancellation at one of our other sites. It's a luxury lodge that we can let you have at the same price if you want it."

"That's marvellous!" Sally enthused, but when she hung up her heart sank. She wouldn't have time to make her usual meticulous plans about what to pack. Normally, she liked to book plenty of activities and interesting local events to keep everyone occupied for two weeks.

Instead they threw all their things haphazardly into the car, the girls plugged in their music and they were off. To her horror, Sally hadn't defrosted the freezer or remembered to cancel the papers. The fortnight stretched ahead, worryingly unplanned and chaotic.

When they arrived at the campsite, it had to be admitted that the luxury lodge was gorgeous and had a sea view. To the girls' delight, it had an outside hot tub as well as a sauna - which was all lovely, but Sally couldn't help fretting about what else they were going to do.

Pete suggested: "Let's simply do nothing for once." He looked tired after the tension and excitement of the last few months.

Sally asked: "What do you mean by nothing?"

"I mean just sit on our deckchairs, eat, drink, and look at the sea."

The girls nodded in eager agreement, but Sally felt a surge of panic. Nothing? What was that about? They would be bored by lunchtime then she would have to come up with some sort of plan to keep them all amused.

nothing

Story by Carmen Nina Walton
Illustration by Kate Davies

Pete said: "You're always so busy, Sal. Why not relax for a change?"

No cooking was needed as the lodge had its own barbecue, so it would be no-frills sausage sandwiches and plain grills. The nearest village was two miles away and the nearest town at least five miles. What on earth was she supposed to do while Pete dozed in his deckchair and the girls went off in search of other teenagers?

Sally felt bereft as she sat on the sun-lounger wishing she had packed a book to read. Gradually, she unwound, looking across at the sea and the distant activity of boats and seagulls. At a nearby caravan, a family was playing a game of Snap that made them laugh joyfully. Below her, on the beach, a woman sat on a bench and pulled out a flask from her backpack.

A dog sat patiently by as she poured out a coffee. From somewhere, the sound of washing flapping in the warm breeze reminded her of childhood.

"Having a nice time?" Pete asked lazily after they had eaten their second barbecue of the day.

"Lovely," Sally replied.

"Great to have nothing to do for a change, eh? I could get used to this."

Sally thought of her daily planning that made sure that everything they needed to do got done and thought to herself, 'Well, I couldn't!' None of them understood the organisation needed to hold the family together, Sally realised, and if she was honest, she wouldn't have it any other way.

But to prove that she really was a good sport, she put a few more sausages on the barbecue.

Poetry Corner

New Year's resolution?

By Sylvia Hicks

I'm going to stop watching the telly
I've decided to give it a rest
I've put on some weight round the belly
So I think it will be for the best

I thought that I might do some knitting
I've got the odd pattern or two
There's plenty of wool in the cupboard
So, perhaps, that will help see me through

I could buy a book and start reading
A novel or thriller to start
I used to be real good at painting
And was told that it came from the heart

I'm really not that good at sewing
And patience was never my thing
but I will give it a go and I will try to sew
Or maybe I could try and sing

I'll go for a walk after dinner
I might even go to the gym
A jog through the park, before it gets dark
And I'm well on the road to get slim

Now there's something I've only just thought of
A job I could possibly do
I'll open a stall in the market
And sell an antique or two

I've plenty of junk in the attic
There's pictures, a sewing machine,
Old handbags, some shoes and a mirror
And things that should never be seen

However, I'm not sure I can do this
I'm feeling quite giddy and sick
I know I'll be sorry if I have to miss Corrie
My decision will have to be quick

I've decided I can't ditch the telly
It's my life after all's said and done
I'll watch what I like
Then get on my bike
And go for a ride in the sun

We coped with the three-day week and proudly sported Afro hairstyles, but what else do you remember about this decade?

1 Starring Frankie Howerd in a skimpy toga, which TV comedy series was made into a film, released in 1971?

2 Which member of the royal family was murdered by the IRA while sailing off the coast of County Sligo in 1979?

3 In which film did Roger Moore first take on the role of James Bond?

4 Which American president was forced to resign over the Watergate affair?

5 In 1979 newsreader Anna Ford was briefly engaged to which ITN news reporter?

6 Accompanied by the band of the Coldstream Guards, Bud Flanagan sang the theme tune of which popular 1970s' sitcom, first aired on July 31, 1968?

7 Who won an Oscar for playing the title role in the Woody Allen film Annie Hall?

8 What was the song that won Abba the 1974 Eurovision Song Contest?

Remember the Seventies?

9 In which year was the first 'test-tube baby' Louise Brown born by caesarean section?

10 Which conflict led to a worldwide shortage of oil and the closure of hundreds of UK petrol stations in 1973?

11 Which music-loving Prime Minister conducted the London Symphony Orchestra?

12 In which year did thousands of Ugandan Asians seek asylum in the UK following a military coup by Idi Amin?

13 Who were the teen idols who wore tartan trews and scarves and had a TV series called Shang-a-Lang?

14 Which book by Richard Adams was a surprise bestseller and later made into a film with the theme tune Bright Eyes sung by Art Garfunkel?

15 From which planet did the Viking spacecraft send back detailed photographs of the terrain in 1976?

16 What was the name of the 'saggy old cloth cat, baggy, and a bit loose at the seams' who won our hearts in 13 TV shows of the same name?

17 In 1974 we were horrified by news reports of widespread famine following disastrous floods in which South Asian country?

18 The sight of a severed horse's head shocked audiences who went to see which hugely acclaimed film starring Marlon Brando?

19 What was the pen name of James Alfred Wight who enjoyed great success with his tales of a vet's life in the fictional Yorkshire town of Darrowby?

20 Lenny Henry, Chris Tarrant and Sally James were the hosts of which Saturday morning TV show for children?

21 Which group topped the bill at the Knebworth Park concert in August 1976?

22 What were the creatures called who lived on Wimbledon Common and urged Make Good Use of Bad Rubbish?

23 Which Radio 2 DJ encouraged his listeners to Fight the Flab?

24 On the night of June 6, 1977, how did the Queen mark the start of the celebrations of her Silver Jubilee?

25 Which two actress friends came up with the idea for the popular period drama Upstairs, Downstairs?

Answers on page 182

PICS: ALAMY

My unlikely

Bringing up a family in a rural caravan was far from luxurious. But Pamela Kwiatkowski only has happy memories...

In 1955, my husband and I arrived in a village on the outskirts of Gloucester. As he was employed in the civil engineering industry we had travelled around up to now, but I was expecting our first child in February 1956, so we decided it was time to put down roots. It proved a wise decision as by 1959 we had three children under four!

We sited our 22ft caravan in a large field. It was very modest compared to today's standards. It had two doors - one led to the lounge, which at night converted into two bedrooms with a double bed in each. The other door led to the kitchen, in which there was a cooker, sink and an Elsan toilet, which had to be emptied and was enclosed in a small compartment.

A solid-fuel stove using coke provided heating and there was Calor gas for lighting and cooking. It was very warm and cosy, providing the stove was kept fuelled all night - otherwise you froze!

An advantage of caravan living was minimal housework, which I hated (and still do). This meant I had plenty of time for the children and exploring the local countryside. This was fortunate as they had little in the way of toys, although my eldest son rode gallantly around the field on a three-wheeled trike, minus tyres, produced by his father out of a skip.

The downside was carrying water, which I collected in a bucket and enamel jug. This involved a round trip of about 300 yards. Washing was all by hand, including nappies. Ironing was done with a flat iron, which if I still had today would probably be an antique.

No TV, but a portable radio for entertainment. So after listening to The Archers at 6.45, it was bath-time and then bed for the children. I had a large baby bath which I also utilised. First of all, legs up under my chin and then over the edge, cowboy film style!

Mail was collected from the post office opposite the site, which was just a room in a cottage. The children came with me and had small packets of sweets and greeted Susie, the postmistress's dog. Most of my shopping was at the local shop. The owner would take my list, price the items and pack them in a cardboard box. Sometimes he added, for free, a ham bone. I could get a few pieces of meat from it and then boil it up for soup. And if money was tight I could have things on tick.

> **An advantage of caravan living was minimal housework...this meant I had plenty of time for the children and exploring the local countryside**

dream home

Caravan living had its ups and downs but Pamela loved the friendships she made and enjoyed having less housework to do

My treat of the week was to push the children to Gloucester, do a bit of shopping and then have lunch in a self-service cafeteria. This was, in total, a walk of about six miles, but it kept my figure in shape and I was able to get right back into my best black skirt after every birth. There were other mums on the site in the same boat.

We socialised together and made sure all the children had birthday parties. My husband never had a holiday during this period, but I went to stay with my mum in my home town of Exeter and the children enjoyed trips in the little local train.

When I went into labour with my third child I was alone in the caravan. My husband had had to go away for work and my older two were being looked after elsewhere. So I crossed a busy road to phone for an ambulance, which took me into hospital where I had the baby. After being discharged I collected the other children and returned to the caravan. My husband did not see the baby until he was six weeks old as his employers only paid for home visits every six weeks. There was no such thing as paternity leave!

In 1962, we were allocated a local authority house, the other side of Gloucester. I hated it. I missed my friends and the amount of housework I needed to do was even more of a horror. The house needed complete redecoration, but our money only stretched to some secondhand furniture – so still no washing machine. It was freezing – remember the long, white winter of 1962-63 – and all we had was an open fire in the living room.

However, when the children were all at school, I was finally able to do some part-time work. I had been trained as a secretary and our financial fortunes improved. But I have happy memories of our caravan life – and sometimes, looking back, it seems like a dream.

Pre-wedding

Katie's wedding plans put Liz in a terrible dilemma

If I could have picked a bride for my son Rob, I couldn't have chosen anyone I liked better than Katie. She was a free spirit - an unconventional, creative girl. You wouldn't think it to look at me now, but I was a bit of a hippie in the Sixties. I was an artist and, yes, I sometimes put flowers in my hair. The floaty clothes that Katie loved were much like the ones I wore back then.

So when she called to ask if she could come round to tell me about the wedding plans, I knew I was going to hear some unusual ideas. I wasn't wrong.

As she sipped her peppermint tea, Katie told me Rob had left all the arrangements to her, saying: "Surprise me. You always do!"

Katie said: "I've had a great idea for the venue."

"Can you let me in on the secret?" I asked.

She beamed. "A butterfly farm!"

I'd been expecting maybe a castle or even a Buddhist temple, but not a butterfly farm.

Katie sighed dreamily. "The weddings take place in an enormous glasshouse filled with exotic flowers and hundreds of butterflies fluttering around."

"Hundreds of butterflies?" I repeated.

"You don't like the idea?" Her face clouded over.

And off she flitted, looking rather like a beautiful butterfly herself ... my heart was sinking. I was going to have to tell her

---

"It sounds wonderful," I said quickly. "But..."

"Oh dear, what's the matter? Do you think Rob will like it?"

"Well, it will certainly be a surprise," I said, trying to sound enthusiastic.

Kate went on: "I could design my own dress with lace butterfly motifs and we could have a cake shaped like a butterfly."

I listened, trying to look as excited as she was, until she looked at her watch and remembered she was due to meet Rob.

"Remember, not a word," she whispered as she left. "It's our secret!"

And off she flitted, looking rather like a beautiful butterfly herself in her red dress. I waved goodbye from the kitchen window, but my heart was sinking. I was going to have to tell her.

I'd have to explain that Rob, my 6ft, rugby-playing son was the bravest man in the world and there was nothing he was scared of, except for one small thing... butterflies.

When he was very young, he had woken one summer night to find one flying frantically around his head. It brushed his face with its wings and his screams brought me running to cuddle and reassure him that there was nothing to fear.

I thought he would grow out of it, but it got worse. I always had to draw his bedroom curtains in case there was a butterfly hiding in the folds. Embarrassed, he begged: "Please, please don't ever tell anyone about it, Mum."

I promised I never would. But his sister knew and teased him unmercifully. She even put a butterfly down the neck of his shirt once which brought on such a bad panic attack I thought Rob would pass out.

I suggested some form of therapy, but he was too ashamed to talk about his phobia to anyone. Then he moved away to work as a fireman in a city where there weren't many butterflies to deal with.

That night I lay awake, tossing and turning. "Jim, how on earth will he cope?" I asked my husband. "It's no good. I'll have to break my promise and tell Katie."

Jim grunted: "Don't interfere, Liz. Rob's a grown man. It's up to him to deal with it."

I kept picturing Rob, running out of his own wedding, sweating and terrified. But would he forgive me if I broke my promise? And would Katie laugh at him - think him less of a man even though he had received an award for his bravery in rescuing two children from a blazing house? I went over and over it in my mind.

Six months before their big day, Rob and Katie came for Sunday dinner.

"So, Rob," I said cautiously, "Katie still hasn't told you where the wedding is going to be?"

He grinned. "No. I've told her to surprise me."

"But he'll find out before the day, of course, as it

nerves

Story by Pru Heathcote
Illustration by Kate Davies

will be on the invitations," Katie said.

That made my mind up. Something would have to be done before those invitations were printed. I rang Katie and invited her round for tea. I don't like lying, but I had no choice. I rehearsed what I would say, 'You see, I'm absolutely terrified of butterflies. I know it's silly, but I can't help it'.

When she arrived, bringing me a bunch of my favourite flowers, Katie took my hand. "Are you okay? You don't look happy."

"Katie, I'm sorry to ruin your plans, but there's something I have to tell you. About the butterfly farm..."

"Oh, that's been cancelled," she said, waving her hand casually.

Relief flooded through me. "Cancelled?"

"Yes, we were having breakfast one day when a butterfly flew in the window. Rob freaked! Then he explained about his phobia."

"Oh, Katie! You don't think any less of him, do you?"

"Of course not. A little thing like that isn't going to change anything."

I smiled. "Except the wedding venue."

"That's all sorted. We were lucky to get a cancellation at St Mark's church. Just for once, I thought it would be nice to do something the conventional way."

Poetry Corner

Our furry hero

By Anita Bush

A dog wandered into our garden one day.
A friendly old mutt, didn't look like a stray.
We never discovered whence he had come,
But we brushed him and fed him and the kids
called him Rum.
Now as family members,
even dogs must work hard.

So we put Rum on duty next door in our yard.
Bright eyed and watchful by night and by day,
But not much of a guard dog, I'm sorry to say.
He barked at the cats and he'd bark at a toad.
He barked at the cattle outside on the road.
He barked at the horses – so where did he fail?
You see, Rum liked people,
and he just wagged his tail.

Then one night when Rum was laid at his ease,
A burglar crept in just as quiet as you please.
But Rum was awake and he'd seen him all right,
Delighted with company this time of the night.
He flew through the yard, his new friend to greet,
And his weight bowled the burglar right off
of his feet.

The intruder got up and ran off with a wail.
With Rum right behind him still wagging his tail.
He departed the yard he'd come in to burgle,
Like a champion athlete clearing a hurdle.
But Rum couldn't jump gates, so, sadly instead,
He picked up the thief's wallet and went back
to bed.

Next morning the evidence everyone viewed,
When Rum brought it to us,
(just a little bit chewed).
Once given the wallet, the police didn't fail,
To capture the burglar and put him in jail.
His confession like wildfire
spread through the town,
How a big vicious guard dog
had knocked the thief down.
There's been no attempts since to burgle our yard,
For everyone knows now that Rum is on guard!

We wore shoulder pads and leg warmers and started watching breakfast TV, but what else do you remember about this decade?

1 First broadcast by Yorkshire Television in 1982, which show was presented for 20 years by Richard 'Twice Nightly' Whiteley?

2 Who said: "Life must go on," after the bombing of the Grand Hotel in Brighton by the IRA in 1984?

3 Which pop star branched into acting in the role of Major Celliers in Merry Christmas, Mr Lawrence?

4 Which husband and wife team designed the wedding dress worn by Princess Diana when she married Prince Charles in St Paul's Cathedral?

5 In which year did the Berlin Wall come down?

6 Dame Judi Dench won an Oscar for playing Queen Elizabeth I in which film?

7 What was the name of the British journalist who was captured in the Lebanon in April 1986 and held hostage for five years?

8 Anneka Rice was voted the female Rear of the Year in 1986, but who was voted top male rear?

Remember the Eighties?

9 Which former Hollywood actor became 40th president of the United States in 1980?

10 Simon le Bon was the singer with which New Wave band that hailed from Birmingham?

11 Pan Am Flight 103 exploded in the air over which Scottish town on December 21, 1988?

12 What was the name given to the day stock exchanges around the world crashed on October 19, 1987?

13 Who was shot outside the Dakota building in New York in December 1980?

14 Guerra de las Malvinas is the Spanish name for which conflict that lasted for ten weeks in 1982?

15 Thanks to the speed of Concorde, which singer managed to perform at both Live Aid concerts in America and England?

16 Which best-selling American writer published his first book, A Time to Kill, in 1989?

17 In 1981, who became known as the 'boat people'?

18 What was the title of the novel that led to author Salman Rushdie receiving death threats from Iran's Ayatollah Khomeini?

19 In the UK, who was the first presenter of the game show The Price is Right?

20 Kew Gardens lost a third of its trees in the gales which hit the British Isles on October 16 of which year?

21 Which pop group was formed specifically to compete in the Eurovision Song Contest which they won with Making Your Mind Up?

22 Which top model, born in Croydon, was discovered in 1988 when she was aged just 14?

23 Winner of 72 caps, Will Carling was the captain of which national rugby team?

24 Which British film about an inspiring political leader won eight Academy Awards in the 1983 Oscars?

25 Popularly known as Beefy, which cricketer walked from John o'Groats to Land's End to raise money for charity?

Answers on page 182

Tizer and

Football, canings and their very own skiffle group. C J Raven looks back with a smile on his time at a Fifties secondary modern

My entrance into secondary modern education at the age of 11 made me feel nervous. Like all of the other 30 boys with me, I was an 11-plus failure. I just did not know what to expect. This was 1955, towards the end of austerity time in Britain and, generally, there was optimistic expectation in the air. But for me, on the day that I entered Silver Street Secondary Modern School for Boys, I felt nothing but apprehension. Some of the other lads looked nervous too.

First of all, we were ushered into class by a junior master. The classroom, with its well-worn desks and the walls painted a sludgy brown and the master's desk, with the efficient-looking cane, gave me a sick feeling. I

> **"Come out here and hold out your hand Raven," said the master. I was sure that I would get the cane for being cheeky**

looked above and it was hard to see a full square foot of white paint. The black and blue blobs of inked blotting paper that had been hurled up there, from the ends of ink-stained rulers, covered most of the ceiling. I sat for a moment, quietly thinking, things can't be that bad here, if you can do things like that.

I was left-handed and it wasn't long before I was caned on the offending hand. It didn't change my habit of writing with my left hand though. But I often think what would be said about such an assault these days.

I soon became friends with the other boys in my class and there was pure delight, when we were together in the off-licence, which was near to the school. The off-licence was often visited by the boys after school and also visited by many of the boys by day. There were sweets to buy, plus sherbet and chocolate powders, broken biscuits, sweet tobacco for rolling, even cigarettes and matches. And the entire selection of Corona drinks. My two favourites were the fizzy drink Tizer and a packet of bubble gum.

Of course I joined the football team. Well, what self-respecting boy wouldn't? When the master in charge of football came round, we had to register our names. One of our team gave his name as E Veasey. "What's your first name lad?" he was asked. Going bright red, Veasey replied, "Well, er, Sir, it's Edwin - but you can call me Eddy - Sir." "Oh, thank you Eddy," replied the master, kindly.

My own embarrassing moment was in the general knowledge class. "Now boys," said the master, "we are going to talk about the invention of the wheel. Can any of you boys tell me, what would be the fundamental property of the wheel?" I had thought up such a clever answer to this question, I was waving my hand about and

bubble gum

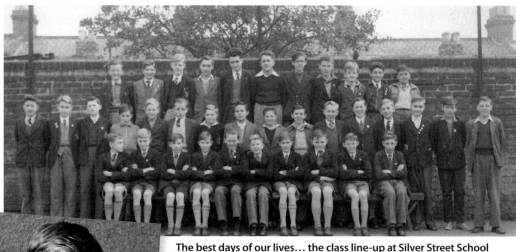

The best days of our lives… the class line-up at Silver Street School

dying to give my answer. "Well Raven," said the master. In that moment, I had forgotten what I was going to say. "Oh, hum-ha - round Sir," I said. "Come out here and hold out your hand Raven," said the master. I was sure that I would get the cane for being cheeky. Instead the master reached forward with a clenched fist and dropped a sweet into my open hand. "A very well thought out answer, Raven," he said.

Gardening, as it was called, took place on the land, to the back of the school playground.

We boys were set to work clearing the ground. The land was full of brambles and roots. And hard work it was too. The work was backbreaking, but we were young and we soldiered on.

I made friends with a boy named Phil Sherman, who became my best friend throughout my school years at Silver Street School. At the age of just 15, he was going to the West End of London and visiting the dance clubs. On asking Phil what he had done at the weekend he would airily reply: "Oh you know, up West - a bit of dancing." Rock 'n' roll? "No," Phil would reply, "the cha-cha." "How do you do that then?" we would ask. And we would gather round to enjoy Phil teaching us the latest dance craze.

By the Christmas of 1958 we had our very own pop group cum skiffle group, comprising a tea chest as bass and a drum-kit

which was a biscuit tin. A piece of sandpaper was stretched over the top of the biscuit tin and a pair of brushes were stroked over the top of the sandpaper, to make a nice shushing sound. Plus, we had a real guitar with three chords. Eddy Veasey did the vocals and we did a very good rendition of, Think it over, the Buddy Holly hit.

When the last day of school came we were given our testimonials. Appropriate words were written about us. Those testimonials were passed round from boy to boy and discussed with much glee and delight.

These days, I often take a walk by the old school. The plot of land that we boys cleared is now a lawn of velvet green. 'We made a good job of that land clearance boys', I murmur to myself. Silver Street School was sometimes the school of hard knocks. But I wouldn't change a day of my time there.

The perfect

Vicky has proudly bought exactly the right present for Secret Santa

Vicky took a Christmas present out of her bag and put it on her desk.

"Ooh, is that your Secret Santa gift?" Emma asked.

"Yup. And this year I've got it right. It's the perfect present."

Emma prodded the beautifully wrapped parcel. "It's really soft. Is it a jumper or something?"

"Yes, it's a jumper or something," Vicky replied with a grin.

"Well, it must be a cheap one - or did you spend more than £10?"

Vicky shook her head. "No, I didn't. I made it myself."

"Really?" Emma raised her eyebrows.

"Yes really, with wool from the pound shop. And you're wasting your time trying to guess who it's for. You'll find out at lunchtime when we do the exchange."

Emma grumbled: "I don't much like this Secret Santa lark. I spend ages trying to find something brilliant but end up settling for something boring because I don't want to get it wrong - like when you gave Dave that bottle of wine last year!"

"Anyway, I've got it right this time. I can't wait to see her face when she opens her Secret Santa"

"That was embarrassing," Vicky agreed, remembering how mortified she had been when Dave pointed out it wasn't the ideal present for a recovering alcoholic.

"Even more embarrassing than the year before when you gave Sally a box of chocolate Brazils!" Emma chuckled.

"Well, I didn't know Sally had a nut allergy, did I?" Vicky defended herself. "Anyway, I've got it right this time. I can't wait to see her face when she opens her Secret Santa."

Emma smiled. "Oh, so it's for a woman, is it? How did you know her size?"

"If you must know, it isn't actually a jumper, but it is something I knitted that I know she needs."

Emma looked around the office. "Is it for someone who works on this floor?"

"No, it's for someone downstairs in Accounts," Vicky lowered her voice. "I wasn't sure who she was when I picked her name from the bag so I went down to do a recce and overheard a conversation that gave me the idea for her present."

"That was lucky!"

"Very! As I walked past her desk I heard her telling someone that she was going to have to get hold of some Valium before Christmas because she is terrified of flying but couldn't avoid it because she was desperate to see Alaska."

"Oh, right," Emma said.

Forgetting her earlier vow of secrecy, Vicky said triumphantly: "I've made her a hat and scarf set! It took longer than I expected so I've been knitting like crazy for the last few evenings, but I'm sure she's going to love it. I mean, it's going to be freezing in Alaska!"

"Well done you! You've put so much thought into your gift that I feel quite guilty," Emma said, turning on her computer ready to start work.

"And I even chose a colour to match her winter coat," Vicky boasted. "I was really chuffed when I spotted Maggie on her way into the office one day wearing a navy coat like mine so I've made the hat and scarf in a pretty pastel blue."

Emma spun round to face her friend. "Did you say Maggie?"

Vicky whispered: "Yes, Maggie Stephenson. You don't know her, do you?"

Emma whispered back: "No, but my mum does. They used to work together years ago and they still meet for coffee now and again."

"And has Maggie told your mum all about her trip to Alaska?"

Emma bit her lip, reluctant to meet her friend's enquiring look. She said: "She isn't going to Alaska, Vicky. Maggie is retiring at the end of the year so she's taking the opportunity to spend a few months with her daughter and baby granddaughter. They live in Australia where it's going to be flipping hot!"

Vicky shook her head. "You must have got it

present

Story by Susan Wright
Illustration by Kate Davies

wrong, Emma. I definitely heard her mention going to see Alaska."

"Yes, you've got that bit right, but Alaska is her granddaughter's name."

Vicky stared at her friend in astonishment. "What sort of name is that for a little girl?"

"She's named after a character in her mother's favourite book," Emma explained. "It's by John Green, I think – 'Looking for Alaska'. It was a bestseller."

Vicky groaned: "So the hat and scarf won't be any good at all. Just my luck. What am I going to do now?"

Emma suggested helpfully: "Well, you could give her a nice see-through washbag filled with little toiletries that you can take on a plane. That would be really useful."

Vicky snapped crossly: "No, I couldn't – it's too late to go out to the shops now, or even online!"

Emma pulled open her desk drawer and took a parcel out. "As it happens, I have the very thing here. I got your name in the draw and I bought this because I remembered you said you might go to Norway to see your brother..."

Vicky's eyes lit up. "We could do a swap!"

"Yes," Emma agreed. "If you don't mind not having a surprise Secret Santa!"

"I don't mind at all," Vicky grinned. The blue hat and scarf had looked amazing when she had tried them on with her own navy coat. For once, she was going to receive the perfect present.

And by a lucky chance, so was Maggie Stephenson!

Poetry Corner

The Hill

By Julie Sharp

How strange to stand on top of this hill
where I haven't stood for so long!
How odd it is to think that this hill
will be here long after I'm gone.

I have a photo of me in this place
it was taken a long time ago.
I was young, and strong and smiling then,
it was winter, I was playing in snow.

But how quickly all those years have gone by
since I was on the hill that cold day,
I could never have seen the joys and sorrows,
that waited for me down life's way.

Now it's late summer, the grass is still green,
the field's full of corn in the valley below,
when I was young was I moved by such beauty?
I cannot recall feeling so.

Now I have time to look at the trees
and the birds that fly high in the sky,
today I can marvel at the plants and flowers
and the butterflies fluttering by.

How glad I am this hill will still be here
long, long after my time is done,
and I pray that the wonder and joy I feel now
will be felt by generations to come!

We bought our first home computers and planned parties to celebrate the Millennium, but what else do your remember about this decade?

1 Which newspaper mogul and former Labour MP drowned when he fell off his yacht in 1991?

2 Which year did the Queen regretfully describe as her 'annus horribilis'?

3 Governor Chris Patten handed over which British territory to the People's Republic of China in June 1997?

4 On February 11, 1990 which 71-year-old human rights activist walked free after 27 years in prison?

5 Which film director scored a monster hit with Jurassic Park, based on a book by Michael Crichton?

6 In which year was the Channel Tunnel opened by the Queen and President Mitterand of France?

7 In 1990, the invasion of which country by Saddam Hussein sparked off the Gulf War between Iraq and the United States?

8 Erected near Gateshead in 1998, the Angel of the North is a massive steel sculpture by which modern artist?

Remember the Nineties?

9 Robbie Williams was a member of which boy band from 1990 to 1996?

10 In 1994 how many women were the first to be ordained as priests in the Church of England?

11 Who played Detective Chief Inspector Jane Tennison in the groundbreaking TV series Prime Suspect?

12 Which mountain in the Lake District was sold for more than £1.7m by the Earl of Lonsdale?

13 Who claimed to have had a four-year affair with John Major while he was Prime Minister?

14 Who were Tinky-Winky, Dipsy, Laa-Laa and Po?

15 In January 1998, who presented Posh Spice with a marquise-shaped diamond ring worth £65,000?

16 Which popular presenter of Gardeners' World died of a heart attack while taking part in a charity bike ride in Wales?

17 The private ownership of handguns was made illegal in the UK after the massacre of sixteen children and their teacher in which Scottish town?

18 Which royal prince made his first official appearance with his parents at Llandaff Cathedral in Wales on St David's Day, 1991?

19 In 1999, what was the name given to the bug causing concern to computer users worldwide?

20 Now better known for his travels by train, which TV personality lost his Conservative seat in the 1997 election?

21 In which year did construction begin on the tourist attraction known as The London Eye?

22 Tina Turner sang the theme tune of the 1995 Bond film GoldenEye, but which Irish actor took over the part of 007?

23 Charles and Chums was one of the titles considered for which British rom-com that launched Hugh Grant's career in 1994?

24 Who was the Czech-born model who stopped the traffic with her 'Hello Boys' ad for Wonderbra?

25 Whose TV cookery programmes brought fame to the Cornish seaside town of Padstow?

26 After a dramatic televised police chase footballer, O J Simpson, was eventually acquitted of what crime?

27 Who wrote the sitcom Dinnerladies and starred in it as Brenda?

Answers on page 182

My wonderful

Elaine Allinson recalls a vanished way of life by the Thames when they lived with her lighterman grandpa and grandma

As a little girl I was blessed with a very cuddly grandpa and a very Victorian grandma, known as Nannie who thought children should be seen and not heard, although I never doubted that she loved me. They were my mum's parents. I have such clear happy memories of my childhood, although I am now in my 90s. My father was a commercial traveller and, at first, we lived in Belfast until I was seven. It was my job to stand on a chair by the front gate to wait for the milkman coming down the road in his pony and trap with huge churns of milk. When I spotted him I'd run in and Mum would come out with two large jugs into which the fresh milk was ladled.

> **A friend of his came dressed as Father Christmas and we were all given a beautifully wrapped present and a balloon**

Dad got a better job, so we returned to England and lived with my grandparents for a while, which is when I really got to know them. Grandpa adored children. By profession he was a lighterman and owned barges and three beautiful shire horses. He had a number of bargees working for him. The yard - as he called it - was where he kept his barges and horses in Brent Meadow Wharf which flowed into the Grand Union Canal and in turn into the Thames near Chiswick.

The bargees took the barges, pulled by the horses into the Thames along the towpath to the East London Docks where they would be loaded with chests of tea and sugar. The return journey went further along the canal to Greenford where J Lyons and Co had a factory, so the tea could be packed and dispatched to retailers.

Every Christmas, Grandpa gave a very lavish party for the bargees' children. My siblings and I were also invited. A friend of his came dressed as Father Christmas and we were all given a beautifully wrapped present and a balloon. Nannie had chosen the presents on a special shopping trip to Barkers in Kensington High Street. She went by taxi, as they never owned a car. They were wrapped in green paper for the boys and red for the girls and delivered to the wharf on the party morning.

Each Christmas we grandchildren were taken by taxi with Nannie, Mum and Dad to Bertram Mills' circus at Olympia and to the pantomime at the Chiswick Empire. Grandpa was always happy when he knew we were having fun.

On Boat Race day, Grandpa filled a barge with all sorts of goodies to eat and drink and we were allowed to invite our friends. Once settled in the barge the horse pulled it along the Thames to Mortlake where it anchored. After we had stuffed ourselves (no parents there to restrain us), we waited excitedly for the two crews to appear and cross the finishing line. I always shouted for Oxford - and still do as one of my grandsons went to Oxford to do an engineering degree.

Grandpa eventually sold out to J Lyons & Co, as his arthritis got the better of him and walking became very painful. He bought

grandpa

Grandpa sits in the front row on the left of Elaine at her sister's wedding. Her Victorian Nannie is front right

a large flat in Chiswick and most Sundays after church we went to their flat for lunch. We always had two roast chickens and our pudding was lashings of different-flavoured Lyons ice-cream.

My later memories of him are of a big, jovial man sitting in a huge blue-plush armchair and always giving us a big hug and kiss. Afterwards he would light his Havana cigar and sit there contentedly smoking and letting the ash fall down his front.

My friend Monica, who joined in most of the things he arranged for us, loved him as much as we did, as she'd never known her grandparents. One day, she and I set off on our bikes with a picnic, through country lanes and sat

by a chain-link fence hoping to see an aeroplane at the new London airport. When we told Grandpa he just chuckled and said:
"What for?"

I joined the ATS at the beginning of World War II and was posted to the army pay office in Manchester. I received the sad news of Grandpa's death on July 21, 1944. I did manage to get a 48-hour pass to go to Grandpa's funeral and felt so proud to salute such a lovely man as he was laid to rest.

Nannie went to live with Mum and Dad as her arthritis got worse and she became wheelchair bound. Their beautiful home was bulldozed down to make room for the Chiswick flyover. That's progress?

Brain teaser answers

Page 39

1	5	2	8	4	9	6	3	7
6	7	9	3	5	1	8	2	4
4	8	3	7	2	6	1	5	9
7	9	8	6	1	2	5	4	3
3	4	5	9	8	7	2	1	6
2	1	6	5	3	4	9	7	8
9	6	4	2	7	5	3	8	1
5	3	7	1	9	8	4	6	2
8	2	1	4	6	3	7	9	5

Page 41

1 Milestone,
2 Sightseer,
3 Simpleton.

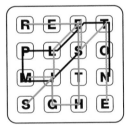

Page 43

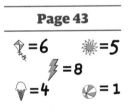

🪁 = 6   ☀ = 5
⚡ = 8
🍦 = 4   🔴 = 1

Page 45

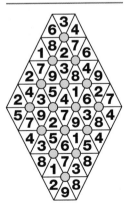

Page 47

1	9	4	6	7	2	5	3	8
8	3	7	4	1	5	6	9	2
6	2	5	9	3	8	1	4	7
9	5	2	1	4	6	7	8	3
4	6	8	7	5	3	2	1	9
7	1	3	8	2	9	4	5	6
2	7	1	3	8	4	9	6	5
5	8	6	2	9	1	3	7	4
3	4	9	5	6	7	8	2	1

Page 49

1 Furtive, 2 Virtue,
3 Rivet, 4 Tier, 5 Ire,
6 Rile, 7 Litre, 8 Litter,
9 Brittle.

Page 51

Brutal, Clutch,
Gluten, Mouthy,
Neuter, Smutty.
Central letters UT

Page 53

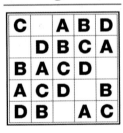

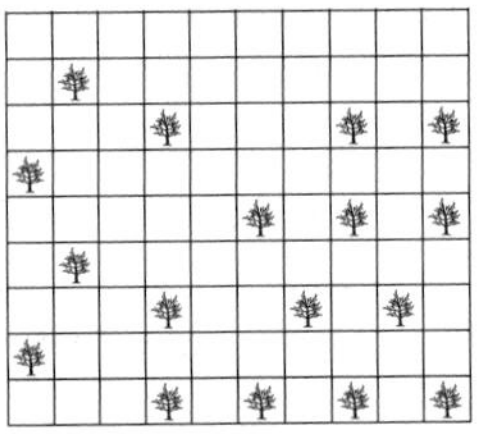

Page 55

Reading across
Stone, Outer, Nurse.
Reading down
Spoon, Otter, Eerie.

Page 57

8	1	7	2	5	9	4	3	6
3	6	9	8	7	4	5	1	2
4	5	2	6	3	1	9	8	7
2	7	5	9	1	8	3	6	4
9	4	8	3	6	7	2	5	1
1	3	6	5	4	2	8	7	9
6	8	4	1	2	5	7	9	3
7	9	1	4	8	3	6	2	5
5	2	3	7	9	6	1	4	8

Page 59

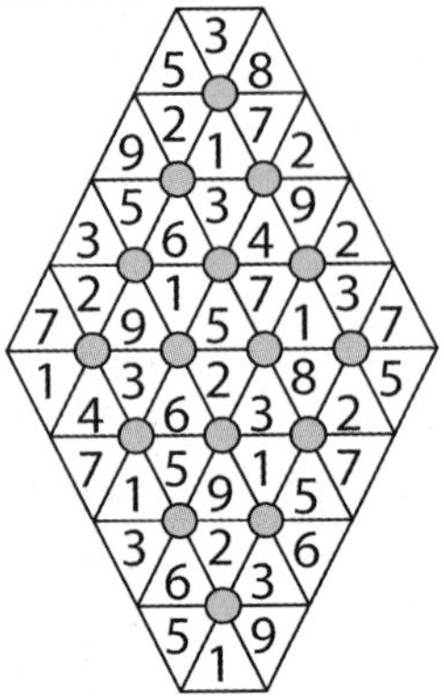

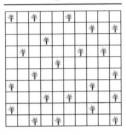

Page 61

The man packed the
cucumber diagonally
into a square package,
with sides of less than
one metre – roughly
0.85 metres long, in fact.

Page 63

■ = 2 ● = 8, ★ = 6,
✚ = 1, ▲ = 3.

Page 65

```
    S A D D L E B A G
A   S     O   C   P   U
M O P   N   L   P U N
P   I S O L A T E   D
H E R     R O T   L E E
I     A     W     L   R
B U T     S E T   A R M
I   I M P R I N T     I
A G O     O   R   I N N
N   N     R E   O     E
    A S C E N D I N G
```

Page 67

2	8	9	4	7	6	1	5	3
7	1	6	3	5	8	4	9	2
5	4	3	2	9	1	6	7	8
6	5	1	8	3	9	2	4	7
8	2	7	1	6	4	5	3	9
3	9	4	7	2	5	8	1	6
9	3	8	5	1	2	7	6	4
1	6	2	9	4	7	3	8	5
4	7	5	6	8	3	9	2	1

Page 69

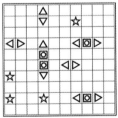

Page 71

1 Leopard, 2 Pedlar,
3 Plead, 4 Deal, 5 Ale,
6 Lace, 7 Clear, 8 Cradle,
9 Declare

Page 73

C		A B D
	D B C A
B A C D
A C D		B
D B		A C

Page 75

(grid puzzle with arrows, stars, circles)

Page 77

3	6	7	9	2	4	5	8	1
1	9	5	7	3	8	6	2	4
8	4	2	6	1	5	9	3	7
2	5	4	8	6	1	3	7	9
6	7	8	2	9	3	1	4	5
9	1	3	5	4	7	8	6	2
7	8	9	4	5	6	2	1	3
4	2	1	3	8	9	7	5	6
5	3	6	1	7	2	4	9	8

Page 79

37 and 62

Page 81

1 John Lennon, 2 Ringo Starr, 3 George Harrison 4 Paul McCartney

Page 83

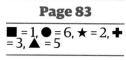 = 1, ● = 6, ★ = 2, ✚ = 3, ▲ = 5

Page 85

The correct password is four. The guest must reply with the number of letters in the word that has been asked of them.

Page 87

6	8	9	2	4	3	1	7	5
2	7	1	9	5	8	3	4	6
4	3	5	7	1	6	2	9	8
7	4	6	1	3	9	8	5	2
5	2	8	4	6	7	9	3	1
1	9	3	5	8	2	4	6	7
3	6	4	8	7	1	5	2	9
9	1	7	3	2	5	6	8	4
8	5	2	6	9	4	7	1	3

Page 89

```
  U N D A U N T E D
P E     U   A   C D
R I G   D   D   O B I
I   O P I N I O N   S
C O T   T A R   O F T
E I     V       M   A
L E A   S A C   I N N
E   T A I L O R S   C
S K I   N   U   I R E
S   O   E   P   N   D
  K N O W L E D G E
```

Page 91

Canopy, Shadow, Future, Quartz, Solemn, Animal, Cleans. Mystery person Natalie Portman

Page 93

Magazine, Man, Mask, Mast, Medals, Mobile phone, Money, Moustache, Mouth, Mug.

Page 95

1 Tetanus, 2 Taunts, 3 Stunt, 4 Nuts, 5 Sun, 6 Onus, 7 Snout, 8 Counts, 9 Consult.

Page 97

8	6	4	9	3	2	1	7	5
1	3	7	4	6	5	9	2	8
9	5	2	1	8	7	4	3	6
6	8	1	2	9	4	3	5	7
4	2	3	7	5	6	8	1	9
5	7	9	3	1	8	6	4	2
3	1	6	5	7	9	2	8	4
2	9	5	8	4	3	7	6	1
7	4	8	6	2	1	5	9	3

Page 99

Across Nappy, Knife, Dread. Down Naked, Prize, Yield.

Page 101

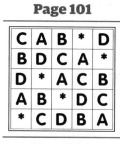

C	A	B	*	D
B	D	C	A	*
D	*	A	C	B
A	B	*	D	C
*	C	D	B	A

Page 103

❄ = 1   ★ = 2
         ♥ = 4
❄ = 5   ◎ = 6

Page 105

Although the initial bill was £15, one of the £5 notes paid is changed into five £1 coins. Therefore, the total the three men ultimately paid is £12, as they get £3 back. So from the £12 the men paid, the chef receives £10 and the waiter receives the £2 difference.
£15 - £3 = £10 + £2.

Page 107

1	3	8	6	4	9	5	2	7
2	5	4	7	8	1	3	9	6
9	7	6	2	3	5	4	8	1
6	2	5	9	1	7	8	4	3
3	9	1	4	2	8	6	7	5
8	4	7	5	6	3	9	1	2
5	1	3	8	7	4	2	6	9
7	8	2	3	9	6	1	5	4
4	6	9	1	5	2	7	3	8

Page 109

M	U	S	I	C
E	R	I	C	A
E	G	G	E	D
T	E	N	D	S

Page 111

Iguana, Tripod, Canary, Chintz, Bamboo, Immune Celebrity: Graham Norton

Page 113

Auntie, Banter, Gentle, Mentor, Syntax, Wanton. Central letters NT

Page 115

Across: Blind, Impel, Gutsy. Down: Being, Input, Delay.

Page 117

3	1	9	5	6	7	4	8	2
8	4	2	9	1	3	7	6	5
5	7	6	8	4	2	9	1	3
2	9	7	6	3	5	1	4	8
4	5	3	1	9	8	2	7	6
1	6	8	7	2	4	3	5	9
6	8	1	3	7	9	5	2	4
7	3	4	2	5	6	8	9	1
9	2	5	4	8	1	6	3	7

Page 119

Beverly Hills, Cape Cod, Colorado Springs, Corpus Christi, Fort Lauderdale, Lake Placid, Little Rock, Long Island, Mount Pleasant, Sioux Falls, Remaining word Green

Page 121

S	H	E	L	F		B	O	A	R
I		X		E		A			E
Z	I	P		V	A	N	D	A	L
E		E		C		R			A
		C		R		O	N	Y	X
P	I	T	Y		A			U	
U			I		S		T	T	
S	Q	U	E	A	K		M	O	W
H			L		E		E		I
Y	A	R	D		W	A	G	O	N

Page 123

1 Chrome, 2 Ignore, 3 Danger, 4 Decade, 5 Grocer, 6 Morose Mystery place Monaco

Page 125

Across: Clean, Actor, Elate Down: Crave, Extra, Nerve

Page 127

7	1	9	8	5	4	3	6	2
4	5	8	6	2	3	7	9	1
2	3	6	1	9	7	4	5	8
6	9	7	5	1	2	8	4	3
5	2	3	7	4	8	9	1	6
1	8	4	9	3	6	2	7	5
9	4	1	3	8	5	6	2	7
8	7	5	2	6	9	1	3	4
3	6	2	4	7	1	5	8	9

Page 129

Page 131

1 Undermine, 2 Splendour, 3 Desperate

Page 133

Across : Table, Error, Today
Down: Treat, Bored, Early

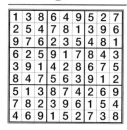

Page 135

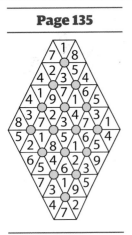

Page 137

4	8	5	9	2	6	3	7	1
7	9	6	8	3	1	5	2	4
3	1	2	4	5	7	6	9	8
2	6	7	1	4	3	8	5	9
8	4	3	6	9	5	2	1	7
1	5	9	7	8	2	4	3	6
5	7	8	2	1	4	9	6	3
6	3	4	5	7	9	1	8	2
9	2	1	3	6	8	7	4	5

Page 139

1 Frosty, 2 Ignore,
3 Length, 4 Deluge,
5 Glider, 6 Silent.
Mystery inventor Edison

Page 141

Baboon, Cyborg, Inborn,
Kibosh, Labour, Nobody.
Central letters BO

Page 143

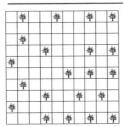

Quiz answers

Remember the Forties?

1 Noel Coward, 2 It's That Man Again, 3 Princess Elizabeth, 4 Aneurin Bevan, 5 1947, 6 A demob suit, 7 Mrs Dale, 8 Brumas, 9 Anne Shelton, 10 Uncle Mac, 11 Blenheim Palace, 12 Denis Compton, 13 Agatha Christie, 14 Wilfred Pickles, 15 Air Raid Precautions, 16 India, 17 The Brains Trust, 18 Clement Attlee, 19 1945, 20 The Wicked Lady, 21 Woolton Pie, 22 Forever Amber, 23 Marguerite Patten, 24 Entertainments National Service Association, 25 Enid Blyton

Remember the Fifties?

1 Stanley Matthews, 2 1952, 3 The Archers, 4 Patience and Prudence, 5 Norman Wisdom, 6 Harold Macmillan, 7 The Festival of Britain, 8 Blue Peter, 9 Tetley, 10 The Daily Mirror, 11 Waitrose, 12 Shirley Bassey, 13 Norman Hartnell, 14 Tony Hancock, 15 Aldermaston (the Atomic Weapons Research Establishment), 16 Cliff Richard, 17 Alec Issigonis, 18 Colonel John Hunt, 19 Carousel, 20 Virginia McKenna, 21 He ran a mile in under four minutes, 22 The Dalai Lama, 23 They were the first animals to return alive from travel in space, 24 Johnny Ray, 25 John Fitzgerald Kennedy

Remember the Sixties?

1 World Wide Fund for Nature, 2 Cliveden, 3 Truman Capote, 4 William Hartnell, 5 The Sun, 6 Lulu, 7 Aberfan, 8 Brian, 9 Golden Wonder, 10 1968, 11 Harold Wilson, 12 The Torrey Canyon, 13 Alec Rose, 14 The Great Train Robbery, 15 Martin Luther King, 16 Toulouse, 17 He performed the first successful human heart transplant, 18 Lyndon Johnson, 19 Puppet on a String, 20 Mods and Rockers, 21 Goldie the golden eagle, 22 That Was The Week That Was, 23 Miss Read, 24 Una Stubbs, 25 The Carpetbaggers

Remember the Seventies?

1 Up Pompeii, 2 Earl Mountbatten, 3 The Man with the Golden Gun, 4 Richard Nixon, 5 Jon Snow, 6 Dad's Army, 7 Diane Keaton, 8 Waterloo, 9 1978, 10 The Arab-Israeli War, 11 Edward Heath, 12 1972, 13 The Bay City Rollers, 14 Watership Down, 15 Mars, 16 Bagpuss, 17 Bangladesh, 18 The Godfather, 19 James Herriot, 20 Tiswas, 21 The Rolling Stones, 22 The Wombles, 23 Terry Wogan, 24 She lit a bonfire beacon at Windsor, 25 Jean Marsh and Eileen Atkins

Remember the Eighties?

1 Countdown, 2 Margaret Thatcher, 3 David Bowie, 4 David and Elizabeth Emanuel, 5 1989, 6 Shakespeare in Love, 7 John McCarthy, 8 Michael Barrymore, 9 Ronald Reagan, 10 Duran Duran, 11 Lockerbie, 12 Black Monday, 13 John Lennon, 14 The Falklands War, 15 Phil Collins, 16 John Grisham, 17 Vietnamese refugees fleeing from a Communist regime by sea 18 The Satanic Verses, 19 Leslie Crowther, 20 1987, 21 Bucks Fizz, 22 Kate Moss, 23 England, 24 Gandhi, 25 Ian Botham,

Remember the Nineties?

1 Robert Maxwell, 2 1992, 3 Hong Kong, 4 Nelson Mandela, 5 Steven Spielberg, 6 1994, 7 Kuwait, 8 Antony Gormley, 9 Take That, 10 Thirty-two, 11 Helen Mirren, 12 Blencathra, 13 Edwina Currie, 14 The Teletubbies, 15 David Beckham, 16 Geoff Hamilton, 17 Dunblane, 18 Prince William, 19 The Millennium Bug, 20 Michael Portillo, 21 1998, 22 Pierce Brosnan, 23 Four Weddings and a Funeral, 24 Eva Herzigova, 25 Rick Stein, 26 The murder of his former wife and her friend Ronald Goldman, 27 Victoria Wood